Basic Optimisation Methods

Brian D. Bunday, B.Sc., Ph.D., F.S.S., F.I.M.A.

School of Mathematical Sciences, University of Bradford

Edward Arnold

First published 1984 by
Edward Arnold (Publishers) Ltd
41 Bedford Square, London WC1B 3DQ

Edward Arnold
300 North Charles Street, Baltimore,
MD21201, USA

Edward Arnold (Australia) Ltd.,
80 Waverley Road, Caulfield East,
Victoria 3145, Australia

ISBN: 0 7131 3506 9

To Harry Moore, the late Reginald Stone and Philip Wood, three fine schoolteachers to whom I shall always be indebted.

Computer typeset by SB Datagraphics, printed and bound by Spottiswoode Ballantyne, Colchester and London

Preface

This book provides a first course in optimisation which should be suitable for undergraduate and postgraduate students who have a sound knowledge of *n* variable calculus and who are also conversant with the computer language BASIC. The emphasis is placed on the thinking that transforms a theoretical idea into a practical computational procedure. Although all the methods have been made plausible, mathematical rigour has been made secondary to the main aim of producing algorithms capable of implementation on a microcomputer.

It is hoped that the reader will make a real effort to get involved with the programs. It is not claimed that they could not be improved. In this way he or she will gain a deeper insight into the ideas underlying the methods and the practical problems that have to be solved when one tries to apply them in a real situation.

Not all the methods that are available have been discussed. However, it is hoped that those that have been selected cover the more important ideas underlying optimisation procedures. Much still remains to be done and I hope that some readers will be stimulated into making their own contributions towards improving the methodology of the subject.

A few remarks about BASIC and the way in which it is used in this book are appropriate. The programs have been written in such a way that they should run with the minimum of fuss on any microcomputer. Thus no attempt has been made to include colour, sound or high resolution graphics.

In the assignment statements LET has been omitted. On some computers it is obligatory and so would have to be inserted. The THEN has been included in IF ... THEN GOTO statements, although on some computers either the THEN or the GOTO may be omitted. No use has been made of the IF ... THEN ... ELSE or the REPEAT ... UNTIL ... facilities as these are not universally available. It is assumed that arrays start at a zero suffix. On machines whose arrays start with suffix 1 some changes would be necessary. One way which should always work is to increase *all* of the suffices including those in the DIM statements by 1. Thus DIM A(M) becomes DIM A(M + 1); B(K, L) becomes B(K + 1, L + 1). However, in particular cases the reader might well find more elegant modifications. The numerical answers given are those obtained on a PET. Some machines which store numbers to a different accuracy will not precisely reproduce the results given here although the differences should only occur in the least significant digits.

Finally it is a pleasure to thank Mrs Valerie Hunter who transformed a rather messy manuscript into a neat and tidy typescript.

BRIAN BUNDAY
1984

Contents

Introduction

This book is concerned with methods for finding the optimum value (maximum or minimum) of a function $f(x_1, x_2, \dots x_n)$ of n real variables. If the function refers to the profit obtained by producing quantities x_i of products P_i it may well be that our desire is to maximise the function. If on the other hand it refers to costs involved in an operation we should probably want to minimise the function. From the mathematical point of view there is little point in considering both maximisation and minimisation, since maximising f is equivalent to minimising $-f$. We shall normally confine ourselves to minimisation.

The values of the variables may be constrained or unconstrained. If, for example, they do indeed refer to the quantities of particular products that we can produce, there will be limits on our production capacity and the quantities that the market can absorb. Thus any solution to our optimisation problem must take account of these constraints. For convenience Part I deals with problems in which the variables are not constrained; Part II considers problems where the variables are constrained.

In any practical optimisation problem there are many overlapping phases. Modelling the physical situation under consideration so as to derive the mathematical function to be minimised, along with the constraints, if any, on the variables, is vital. Then an appropriate procedure for carrying out the minimisation has to be chosen. This procedure has to be implemented in practice and in many real situations this will involve programming a computer to carry out extensive calculations. Finally, the mathematical result has to be interpreted back in terms of the physical context of the problem.

Although it is not intended to neglect totally any of these phases, the main thrust of this book is to emphasise the procedures which are available to carry out the minimisation process, and to discuss the ways in which such procedures can be transformed into organised calculations capable of being carried out by a computer.

It is no accident that many of the important methods have developed over the last three decades, a period that has witnessed the advent of the digital computer. The methods are computer methods. It is difficult to envisage them being of any real practical value without an extremely fast and efficient calculator being available. Many main-frame computers will have optimisation packages which implement these methods. These can be very efficient and allow a wide range of problems to be solved. They can, however, be a little remote, and can be used without an appreciation of what is really going on.

The advent of the microcomputer into the home and classroom has meant that the user can get more intimately involved with the computer program. From the student's point of view this involvement can lead to a keener appreciation of the methodology and its computer implementation. For most of the methods discussed in this book (it is not claimed that the list of such methods is exhaustive) computer programs in the language BASIC have been included. A full explanation of the derivation and coding for these programs is given and they should give the student a new insight into the real application of optimisation methods.

The programs have been well tested over many years of teaching courses of this type at Bradford University. The author would not claim however, that they are the ultimate in elegance and efficiency. As the reader becomes more confident he might well be tempted to improve on the programs, and the author would be interested to hear from readers on this point. The programs should run on most microcomputers which use BASIC or Computer Microsoft. All of the programs have been run on PET and Tandy (TRS80) computers. It would not be a difficut task to 'translate' the programs into other languages such as FORTRAN or ALGOL so that they could be run on main-frame computers.

Part I
Unconstrained Optimisation

1
Classical Methods

1.1 Functions of One Variable

A function $f(x)$ has a local minimum at the value x_0 if there exists a positive value δ such that if $|x - x_0| < \delta$, $f(x) \geqslant f(x_0)$; i.e. if there exists a neighbourhood of x_0 such that for all values of x in this neighbourhood, $f(x)$ is at least as large as $f(x_0)$.

$f(x)$ has a global minimum at x^* if $f(x) \geqslant f(x^*)$ for all values of x.

Figure 1.1 shows a graphical representation of a function $f(x)$. It has a local minimum at x_0 and a global minimum at x^*.

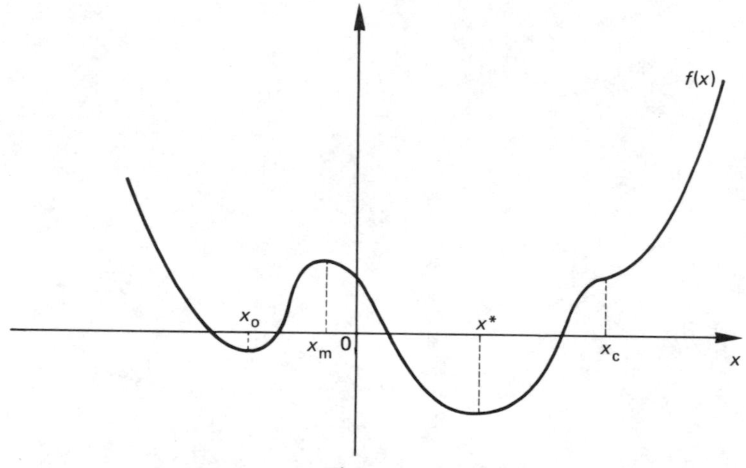

Figure 1.1

The classical approach to the problem of finding the values x_0 and x^* is to find equations which must be satisfied by x_0 and x^*. The function and its derivatives represented in Fig. 1.1 are continuous, and we see that at both x_0 and x^* the derivative $f'(x)$, the gradient of the function, is zero. Thus x_0 and x^* will be solutions of the equation

$$f'(x) = 0. \tag{1.1}$$

The values x_m, at which there is a local maximum, and x_c, at which there is a horizontal point of inflexion also satisfy this equation. Thus equation 1.1 is only a *necessary* condition for a minimum. It is not *sufficient* for a minimum.

However, we notice that at x_0 and x^*, $f'(x)$ changes sign from negative to positive. At x_m the change is from positive to negative whilst at x_c the derivative does not change sign as x passes through the value x_c. Thus at a minimum the derivative is an increasing function and since the rate of increase of $f'(x)$ is measured by the second derivative we shall expect

$$f''(x_0) > 0, \quad f''(x^*) > 0 \quad \text{while } f''(x_m) < 0.$$

If, however, the second derivative is zero the situation remains ambiguous.

The intuitive results above can be put on a firmer footing by considering the Taylor series expansion of $f(x)$ about x_0 (or x^* or x_m). This of course calls for continuity of $f(x)$ and its derivatives.

$$f(x_0 + h) - f(x_0) = hf'(x_0) + \frac{h^2}{2!}f''(x_0) + \ldots \tag{1.2}$$

If x_0 gives a minimum the left hand side is non-negative for all $h(|h| < \delta)$ however small. Thus $f'(x_0)$ must be zero and this is the necessary condition (equation 1.1). For if it were positive a sufficiently small negative h value would make the right hand side negative, and if it were negative a sufficiently small positive h value would make the right hand side negative.

Since the next term involves h^2 we see that if

$$f''(x_0) > 0 \tag{1.3}$$

we shall indeed have a minimum. If $f'(x_m) = 0$ and $f''(x_m) < 0$ then by similar arguments x_m gives a maximum. We should have to compare $f(x_0)$ and $f(x^*)$ to distinguish between the local and the global minimum.

Example 1

Examine the nature of the turning points of the function $f(x) = x^3 - 2x^2 + x + 1$.

$$f'(x) = 3x^2 - 4x + 1 = 0$$

when

$$(3x - 1)(x - 1) = 0$$

$$\text{i.e.} \quad x = \tfrac{1}{3} \quad \text{or} \quad x = 1.$$

When $x = \frac{1}{3}$, $f'(x)$ changes sign from positive to negative. When $x = 1$, $f'(x)$ changes sign from negative to positive. Thus $x = \frac{1}{3}$ gives a maximum and $x = 1$ gives a minimum.

In this example it might be easier to resolve the situation by considering the second derivative

$$f''(x) = 6x - 4.$$

$$f''(\tfrac{1}{3}) = -2 \text{ is negative;} \quad x = \tfrac{1}{3} \text{ gives a maximum.}$$

$$f''(1) = 2 \text{ is positive;} \quad x = 1 \text{ gives a minimum.}$$

The ambiguous case where $f''(x) = 0$ can be settled when it arises by continuing the Taylor series expansion:

$$f(x_0 + h) - f(x) = hf'(x_0) + \frac{h^2}{2!}f''(x_0) + \frac{h^3}{3!}f'''(x_0) + \frac{h^4}{4!}f''''(x_0) + \cdots$$

We can then derive the rule:

> if $f(x)$ and its derivatives are continuous then x_0 is an extreme point (maximum or minimum) if and only if n is even, where n is the order of the first non-vanishing derivative at x_0. If $f^n(x_0) < 0$, x_0 gives a maximum; if $f^n(x_0) > 0$, x_0 gives a minimum.

Example 2

Find the turning point of $f(x) = (x-1)^6$.

$$f'(x) = 6(x-1)^5 = 0 \quad \text{when } x = 1.$$

$f^6(1) = 6!$ is the first non-vanishing derivative at $x = 1$. Thus $f(x)$ has a minimum when $x = 1$.

1.2 Functions of *n* Variables

We consider the function of n real variables

$$f(x_1, x_2, x_3, \ldots, x_n) = f(\mathbf{x}).$$

The point with co-ordinates $(x_1, x_2, \ldots, x_n)$ in n dimensional Euclidean space is denoted by the column vector $\mathbf{x}$. The gradient of the function, i.e. the vector with components $(\partial f/\partial x_1, \partial f/\partial x_2, \ldots, \partial f/\partial x_n)$ is denoted by $\nabla f(\mathbf{x})$ or sometimes $\mathbf{g}(\mathbf{x})$. The Hessian matrix of $f(\mathbf{x})$ is denoted by $\mathbf{G}(\mathbf{x})$ and is the symmetric $n \times n$ matrix with elements

$$G_{ij} = \frac{\partial^2 f}{\partial x_i \partial x_j}.$$

$f(\mathbf{x})$ has a local minimum at $\mathbf{x}_0$ if there exists a neighbourhood of $\mathbf{x}_0$ such that $f(\mathbf{x})$ is at least as large as $f(\mathbf{x}_0)$ for all points in the neighbourhood; i.e. there exists a positive δ such that for $|\mathbf{x} - \mathbf{x}_0| < \delta$, $f(\mathbf{x}) \geqslant f(\mathbf{x}_0)$.

For the global minimum $\mathbf{x}^*$, $f(\mathbf{x}) \geqslant f(\mathbf{x}^*)$ for all $\mathbf{x}$.

With these definitions and certain differentiability assumptions we can generalise equation 1.2 to give

$$\begin{aligned} f(\mathbf{x}_0 + \mathbf{h}) - f(\mathbf{x}_0) &= \sum_{i=1}^{n} h_i \frac{\partial f}{\partial x_i}(x_1, \ldots, x_n) + \frac{1}{2!} \sum_{i=1}^{n} \sum_{j=1}^{n} h_i h_j \frac{\partial^2 f}{\partial x_i \partial x_j}(x_1, \ldots, x_n) + \cdots \\ &= \mathbf{h}^{\mathrm{T}} \nabla f(\mathbf{x}_0) + \tfrac{1}{2} \mathbf{h}^{\mathrm{T}} \mathbf{G}(\mathbf{x}_0) \mathbf{h} + \cdots \end{aligned} \tag{1.4}$$

Then if $\mathbf{x}_0$ gives a minimum for $f(\mathbf{x})$ each of the first partial derivatives $\partial f/\partial x_i$ $(i = 1, \ldots, n)$ must vanish at $\mathbf{x}_0$. For if not, by choosing h_i appropriately we could make $f(\mathbf{x}_0 + \mathbf{h}) - f(\mathbf{x}_0)$ negative.

Thus a necessary condition for a minimum at $\mathbf{x}_0$ is

$$\nabla f(\mathbf{x}_0) = \mathbf{0} \tag{1.5}$$

$$\text{i.e.} \quad \frac{\partial f(x_0)}{\partial x_i} = 0 \quad (i = 1, \ldots, n). \tag{1.6}$$

Then the sign of $f(\mathbf{x}_0 + \mathbf{h}) - f(\mathbf{x}_0)$ is determined by that of

$$\tfrac{1}{2} \mathbf{h}^{\mathrm{T}} \mathbf{G}(\mathbf{x}_0) \mathbf{h}. \tag{1.7}$$

If $\mathbf{G}(\mathbf{x}_0)$ is positive definite this is positive for all $\mathbf{h}$. Thus necessary and sufficient conditions for a minimum are

$$\nabla f(\mathbf{x}_0) = \mathbf{0}, \quad \mathbf{G}(\mathbf{x}_0) \text{ positive definite.} \tag{1.8}$$

For a maximum we require

$$\nabla f(\mathbf{x}_m) = \mathbf{0}, \quad \mathbf{G}(\mathbf{x}_m) \text{ negative definite.} \tag{1.9}$$

Example 1

Examine the extreme point(s) of

$$f(\mathbf{x}) = x_1^2 + x_2^2 + x_3^2 - 4x_1 - 8x_2 - 12x_3 + 100.$$

$$\nabla f(\mathbf{x}) = \begin{pmatrix} 2x_1 - 4 \\ 2x_2 - 8 \\ 2x_3 - 12 \end{pmatrix} = \mathbf{0} \quad \text{when } x_1 = 2, x_2 = 4, x_3 = 6.$$

$$\mathbf{G}(\mathbf{x}) = \begin{pmatrix} 2 & 0 & 0 \\ 0 & 2 & 0 \\ 0 & 0 & 2 \end{pmatrix}$$ is positive definite. All the eigenvalues are positive at 2.

Thus (2, 4, 6) is a minimum of $f(\mathbf{x})$.

1.3 Newton's Method

For functions of one variable the classical approach finds the values of x at the turning points of $f(x)$ as the solutions of the equation

$$f'(x) = 0.$$

This equation may not be easy to solve. We therefore consider briefly a numerical method for its solution. A rough sketch of the curve $y = f'(x)$ may allow us to obtain an approximate solution. If we can find two values a and b such that $f'(a)$ and $f'(b)$ have opposite signs, then, subject to certain continuity assumptions, there will be a root η of the equation, with $a < \eta < b$ (see Fig. 1.2).

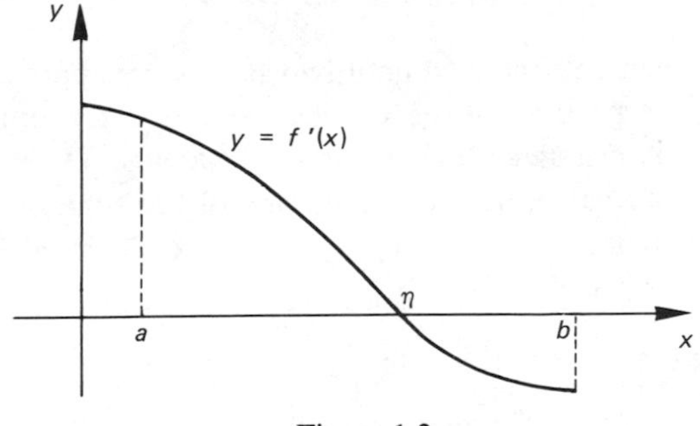

Figure 1.2

Newton's method enables us to improve on a relatively crude approximation to a root of the equation $\phi(x) = 0$. [$\phi(x) \equiv f'(x)$ in the context of our problems.] In Fig. 1.3, x_0, the x co-ordinate of P, is an approximation to the root of $\phi(x) = 0$. Let PT be the tangent at P on the curve and T the point where the tanget meets the x- axis.Then in general OT will be a better approximation to the root which is at K.

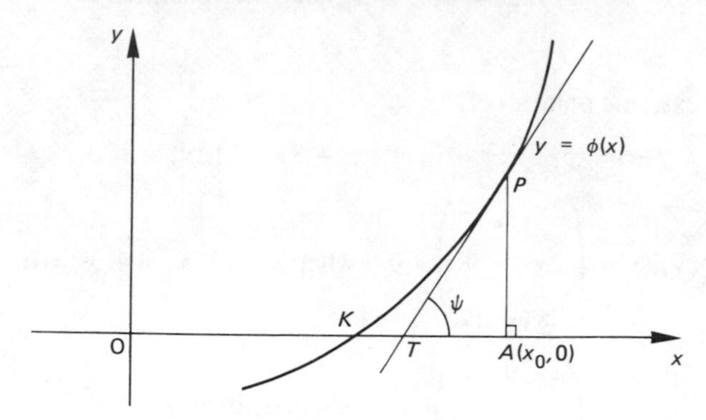

Figure 1.3

Now $OT = OA - TA = x_0 - TA$. Also

$$\frac{PA}{TA} = \tan \psi = \phi'(x_0).$$

$$\therefore \quad TA = \frac{PA}{\phi'(x_0)} = \frac{\phi(x_0)}{\phi'(x_0)}$$

$$\therefore \quad x_1 = x_0 - \frac{\phi(x_0)}{\phi'(x_0)}$$

We can similarly improve upon x_1,

$$x_2 = x_1 - \frac{\phi(x_1)}{\phi'(x_1)}$$

and in general

$$x_{r+1} = x_r - \frac{\phi(x_r)}{\phi'(x_r)}. \tag{1.10}$$

The recalculations can be continued until two successive approximations agree to the required accuracy. The program given carries out this algorithm. It is general in the sense that $F = \phi(x)$ is evaluated at subroutine 1ØØØ and $D = \phi'(x)$ is evaluated at subroutine 2ØØØ for any value of x. The accuracy of the solution can be set by giving E a sufficiently small value. $FF = f(x)$ $[f'(x) = \phi(x)]$ is evaluated at subroutine 3ØØØ.

```
READY.

1Ø PRINT "PROGRAM TO FIND TURNING POINTS OF F(X)"
2Ø REM F(X) EVALUATED AT 3ØØØ
3Ø REM F'(X) EVALUATED AT 1ØØØ
4Ø REM F''(X) EVALUATED AT 2ØØØ
5Ø PRINT"ACCURACY REQUIRED":INPUT E
6Ø PRINT"INITIAL VALUE":INPUT Z
7Ø PRINT "":PRINT"SUCCESSIVE APPROXIMATIONS"
8Ø X=Z
9Ø GOSUB 1ØØØ:GOSUB 2ØØØ
1ØØ Z=X-F/D
11Ø PRINT X,Z
```

```
120 IF ABS(Z-X)>E THEN GOTO 80
130 PRINT"    FINAL SOLUTION    "
140 X=Z:GOSUB 1000:GOSUB 2000:GOSUB 3000
150 IF D>0 THEN PRINT"MINIMUM"FF"AT"X:GOTO 200
160 IF D<0 THEN PRINT"MAXIMUM"FF"AT"X:GOTO 200
200 END
1000 F=X-COS(X)
1010 RETURN
2000 D=1+SIN(X)
2010 RETURN
3000 FF=X*X/2-SIN(X)
3010 RETURN
READY.
```

Example 1

Find the minimum of $y = \frac{1}{2}x^2 - \sin x$.

The subroutines as listed are appropriate.

$$f(x) = \tfrac{1}{2}x^2 - \sin x$$

$$\phi(x) = f'(x) = x - \cos x = 0 \quad \text{when } x = 0{\cdot}7391$$

from the output below.

$$\phi'(x) = 1 + \sin x \quad \text{which is positive when } x = 0{\cdot}7391.$$

Thus the minimum of y is $-0{\cdot}4005$ when $x = 0{\cdot}7391$ to 4 decimal places.

```
PROGRAM TO FIND TURNING POINTS OF F(X)
ACCURACY REQUIRED    0.00001
INITIAL VALUE        0.5

SUCCESSIVE APPROXIMATIONS
 .5                .755222417
 .755222417                  .739141666
 .739141666                  .739085134
 .739085134                  .739085133
    FINAL SOLUTION
MINIMUM-.400488612 AT .739085133
```

Newton's method will fail if the first approximation to the root is such that the value of $\phi(x_0)/\phi'(x_0)$ is not small enough (see Fig. 1.4). The usual remedy is to improve the initial approximation to the root when the iterations will generally converge.

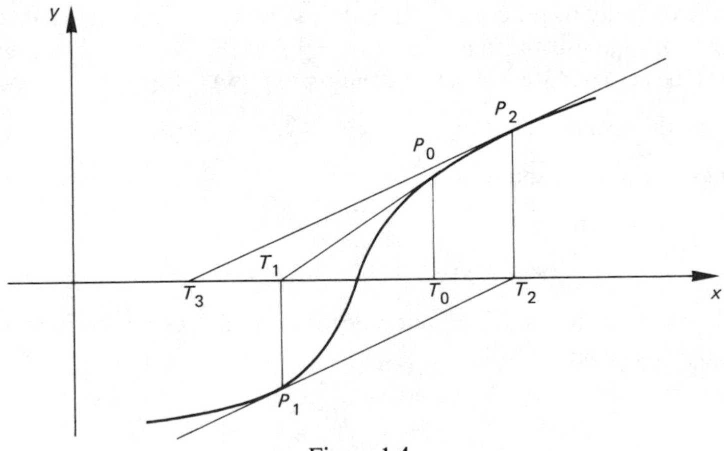

Figure 1.4

Exercises 1

1. Find the maximum and minimum values of $f(x) = x(x-1)^2$.

2. Find the maximum and minimum values of $f(x) = x/(x^2+1)$.

3. Show that the minimum value of $a \cos\theta + b \sin\theta$ is $-\sqrt{(a^2+b^2)}$. Can you do this without involving the derivative?

4. An isosceles triangle of vertical angle 2θ is inscribed in a circle of radius r. Find an expression for the area of the triangle as a function of θ and show that this is a maximum when the triangle is equilateral.

5. Consider the function $f(x) = x^{2/3} - 1$. Sketch its graph. Show that $f(x)$ has a minimum when $x = 0$. What is the value of $f'(x)$ when $x = 0$? Does $f'(x)$ change sign as x increases through the value 0?

6. Consider the function $f(x) = |x|$. Find its minimum value. What can you say about $f'(x)$ at this value?

7. Find the minimum value of $-e^{-x} \sinh(x/2)$.

8. When a production run is made to produce a quantity of a certain commodity there is a set up cost of £K. The commodity is held in stock until it is used and the cost of holding 1 unit in stock is £S per unit time. The commodity is used at a uniform rate R per unit time. Show that if it is produced regularly in lots of size x at time intervals x/R then the cost per unit time of running this system is

$$C = \frac{KR}{x} + \frac{Sx}{2}.$$

Show that C is minimised by choosing $x = \sqrt{2KR/S}$.

9. Examine the turning values of $f(x) = x^4 - 14x^3 + 60x^2 - 70x$. [This simple looking example illustrates one of the problems with the classical approach. We have to solve the equation $f'(x) = 0$. In this case it is a cubic which does not easily factorise. Paradoxically one way to proceed might be to use one of the numerical methods of the next chapter to minimise the function $\phi(x) = [f'(x)]^2$. When $\phi(x)$ is minimised, its minimum will be zero and we will have a solution to $f'(x) = 0$.]

10. Examine the turning points of $f(\mathbf{x}) = x_1^2 + 4x_1x_2 + 5x_2^2$.

11. Examine the turning points of $-x_1^2 - 6x_2^2 - 23x_3^2 - 4x_1x_2 + 6x_1x_3 + 20x_2x_3$.

12. $f(\mathbf{x})$ is the quadratic function

$$f(\mathbf{x}) = a + \mathbf{b}^{\mathrm{T}}\mathbf{x} + \tfrac{1}{2}\mathbf{x}^{\mathrm{T}}\mathbf{G}\mathbf{x}$$

where a is a constant, $\mathbf{b}$ is a vector independent of $\mathbf{x}$, and $\mathbf{G}$ is a positive definite symmetric matrix independent of $\mathbf{x}$.
Show that

$$\mathbf{x}^* = -\mathbf{G}^{-1}\mathbf{b}.$$

13. Show that the function $f(\mathbf{x}) = (x_1 - a)^2 + (x_2 - b)^2 + (x_3 - c)^2$ has a minimum at (a, b, c).

14. $f(\mathbf{x}) = f(x_1, x_2)$ has a minimum at (x_1^*, x_2^*). Show that the conditions 1.8 become

$$\frac{\partial f}{\partial x_1}(x_1^*, x_2^*) = 0; \quad \frac{\partial f}{\partial x_2}(x_1^*, x_2^*) = 0,$$

$$\frac{\partial^2 f}{\partial x_1^2}(x_1^*, x_2^*) > 0,$$

$$\frac{\partial^2 f}{\partial x_1^2}(x_1^*, x_2^*)\frac{\partial^2 f}{\partial x_2}(x_1^*, x_2^*) - \left[\frac{\partial^2 f}{\partial x_1 \partial x_2}(x_1^*, x_2^*)\right]^2 > 0.$$

15. A firm manufactures two similar products I and II. The costs of production are $c_i q_i$ $(i = 1, 2)$ where c_i are constants and the q_i are the sales quantities of the two products. The latter are dependent on the prices (p_1 and p_2) of the two products. Analysis of past sales data has yielded the empirical formulae

$$q_1 = a_1 p_2 - b_1 p_1$$

$$q_2 = a_2 p_1 - b_2 p_2$$

where a_1, a_2, b_1, b_2 are positive constants. It is required to find the values of the prices p_1 and p_2 which maximise the total profits.

Find equations for p_1 and p_2 which maximise the profit and solve them. Show that if the solutions to these equations are positive and $4b_1 b_2 > (a_1 + a_2)^2$ these equations yield optimal prices.

16. Find the minimum of $e^{-x} - \cos x$.

2 Search Methods—Functions of One Variable

2.1 Introduction

Question 9 in Exercise 1 illustrates a common problem that arises with the classical approach. We cannot easily solve the equation $f'(x) = 0$, and have to resort to numerical methods. In this chapter we consider some simple numerical procedures which directly locate the minimum of a function $f(x)$.

With such methods we literally search for the minimum of $f(x)$ in some range $a < x < b$ in which we suspect the minimum lies, by evaluating the function at chosen points in the interval. This strategy may be the only one available. For instance the cost of running a chemical process may depend on the operating temperature. The plant engineer knows that cost is a function of T although he may not have an explicit function. He can, however, experiment and run the process at various temperatures, and hence find the cost at these temperatures and hope in this way to locate the minimum of the cost function, and the temperature at which to run the process for least cost.

We may try to find the position of the minimum by a point approximating it with sufficient accuracy, or we may determine a (short) interval in which the minimum is located. We try to achieve our objective as efficiently as possible, i.e., with as few function evaluations as possible. In the example cited it may not be possible to control the temperature precisely and an accuracy of 1°C or even 10°C may be quite acceptable. However, since it costs money to do an experiment the plant engineer will want to obtain this accuracy with as few experiments as possible.

We assume that we have two values a and b which specify an interval, maybe a very crude one, in which the true minimum point lies, and that within this interval the function is unimodal, i.e. has one minimum at x^*. Thus our function has a form similar to that shown in Fig. 2.1. For such a function, if we know its value at three points

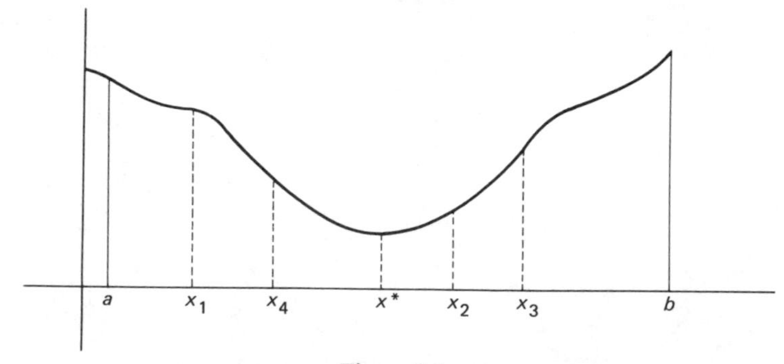

Figure 2.1

$$x_1, x_2, x_3 \quad \text{with} \quad a < x_1 < x_2 < x_3 < b$$

and $f(x_2) < f(x_1)$ and $f(x_2) < f(x_3)$ then

$$x_1 < x^* < x_3.$$

Thus we would have reduced the interval of uncertainty for the position of x^* from (a, b) to (x_1, x_3).

2.2 Fibonacci Search

Suppose that we want to locate the minimum as accurately as possible, i.e. with the shortest possible interval of uncertainty, but can only afford n function evaluations. How should we choose the n values at which we evaluate the function? In the first place it would seem clear that we should not make the decision for all the points at the outset of the exercise. Rather, we should let the function values we obtain from the early experiments determine the position of subsequent points. In effect as we obtain function values, we obtain information about the function and the position of its minimum. We use this information to guide us in our search.

Thus suppose, as in Fig. 2.1, that we have an interval of uncertainty (x_1, x_3) and have a function value $f(x_2)$ within this interval. If we could carry out just one further experiment at the point x_4, where should we place x_4 so as to obtain the smallest possible interval of uncertainty?

Suppose $x_2 - x_1 = L$ and $x_3 - x_2 = R$ with $L > R$ (as in Fig. 2.1) and these will be fixed if x_1, x_2 and x_3 are known. If x_4 is placed in (x_1, x_2) then

(i) if $f(x_4) < f(x_2)$ the new uncertainty interval will be (x_1, x_2) of length $x_2 - x_1 = L$.
(ii) if $f(x_4) > f(x_2)$ the new uncertainty interval will be (x_4, x_3) of length $x_3 - x_4$.

Since we do not know which of these outcomes will occur we choose x_4 so as to minimise the larger of $x_3 - x_4$ and $x_2 - x_1$. We achieve this by making $x_3 - x_4$ and $x_2 - x_1$ equal, i.e., by placing x_4 symmetrically in the interval with respect to x_2, the point already in the interval. Any other position for x_4 *could* result in an interval longer than L. Placing x_4 in this position means that we are not gambling on getting a particular outcome.

If we then found that we were allowed one more evaluation we should apply the same strategy to the interval (x_1, x_2) in which we already have the value at x_4, (i), or (x_4, x_3) in which we already have the value at x_2, (ii). Thus the strategy is clear once we have started. We place the next point within the interval being searched symmetrically with respect to the point already there. Paradoxically, to see how we should start we have to consider how we will finish.

At the nth evaluation we place the nth point symmetrically with respect to the $(n-1)$th point. The position of this latter point is in principle under our control. In order to get the greatest interval reduction at this stage it should bisect the penultimate interval. Then x_n would coincide with x_{n-1}. We appear to have a problem here since no new information is being obtained. In practice x_{n-1} and x_n are separated just sufficiently to enable us to decide which half, left or right, is the final uncertainty interval. They are placed at a distance $\varepsilon/2$ either side of the middle of L_{n-1}; ε may be at our choice or it may be the minimum separation of two points that is possible. (Our plant engineer could only control temperature to the nearest degree perhaps, then $\varepsilon = 1$.)

The interval of uncertainty will be of length L_n and

$$L_{n-1} = 2L_n - \varepsilon. \quad \text{(See Fig. 2.2, bottom layer.)}$$

At the preceding stage x_{n-1} and x_{n-2} must be symmetrically placed within L_{n-2} and distant L_{n-1} from the ends of that interval. Thus

$$L_{n-2} = L_{n-1} + L_n. \quad \text{(See Fig. 2.2, middle layer.)}$$

N.B. As drawn it is evidently x_{n-2} which remains as the included point at the penultimate stage.

Similarly at the previous stage

$$L_{n-3} = L_{n-2} + L_{n-1}. \quad \text{(See Fig. 2.2, top layer.)}$$

In general

$$L_{j-1} = L_j + L_{j+1} \quad \text{for } 1 < j < n. \tag{2.1}$$

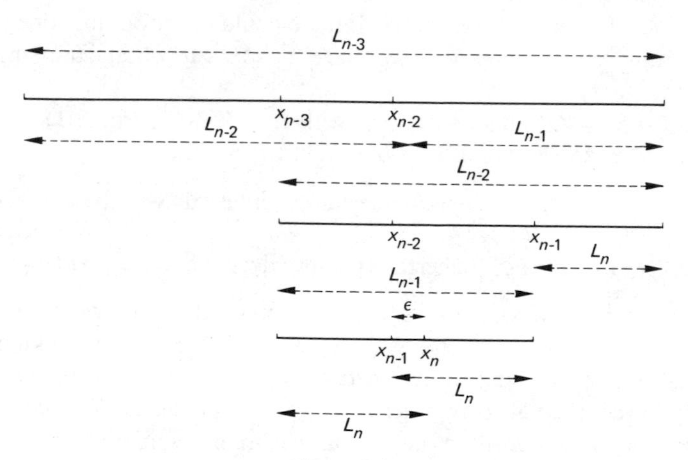

Figure 2.2

Thus

$$L_{n-1} = 2L_n - \varepsilon$$

$$L_{n-2} = L_{n-1} + L_n = 3L_n - \varepsilon$$

$$L_{n-3} = L_{n-2} + L_{n-1} = 5L_n - 2\varepsilon$$

$$L_{n-4} = L_{n-3} + L_{n-2} = 8L_n - 3\varepsilon \quad \text{etc.}$$

If we define the Fibonacci sequence of numbers by $F_0 = 1$, $F_1 = 1$ and $F_k = F_{k-1} + F_{k-2}$ for $k = 2, 3, \ldots$ then

$$L_{n-j} = F_{j+1} L_n - F_{j-1}\varepsilon, \quad j = 1, 2, \ldots, n-1. \tag{2.2}$$

If the original interval (a, b) is of length L_1 $(=b-a)$

$$L_1 = F_n L_n - \varepsilon F_{n-2}$$

$$\text{i.e.} \quad L_n = \frac{L_1}{F_n} + \varepsilon \frac{F_{n-2}}{F_n}. \tag{2.3}$$

Thus with n function evaluations we reduce the original uncertainty interval to a fraction $1/F_n$ of its value (neglecting ε), and this is the best that can be done.

Once the search has begun it is easy to continue using our symmetry rule. Thus we need to find the position of the first point which is placed L_2 units from one end of the original interval. It does not matter which end because the second point is placed L_2 units from the other end by our rule.

$$\begin{aligned} L_2 &= F_{n-1} L_n - \varepsilon F_{n-3} \\ &= F_{n-1} \frac{L_1}{F_n} + \varepsilon \frac{(F_{n-1}F_{n-2} - F_n F_{n-3})}{F_n} \quad \text{by (2.3)} \\ &= \frac{F_{n-1}}{F_n} L_1 + \frac{(-1)^n \varepsilon}{F_n}. \end{aligned} \tag{2.4}$$

(See Question 2 in Exercises 2).

(i) $x_4 < x_2$
$f_4 < f_2$
New interval (x_1, x_2) with x_4 included.
Line 33Ø in program

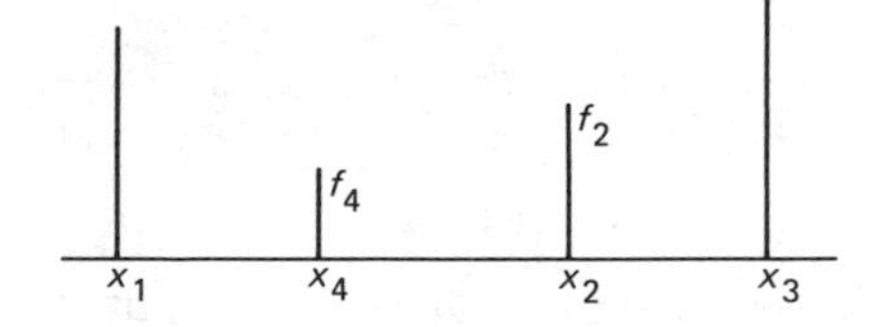

(ii) $x_4 > x_2$
$f_4 < f_2$
New interval (x_2, x_3) with x_4 included.
Line 36Ø in program

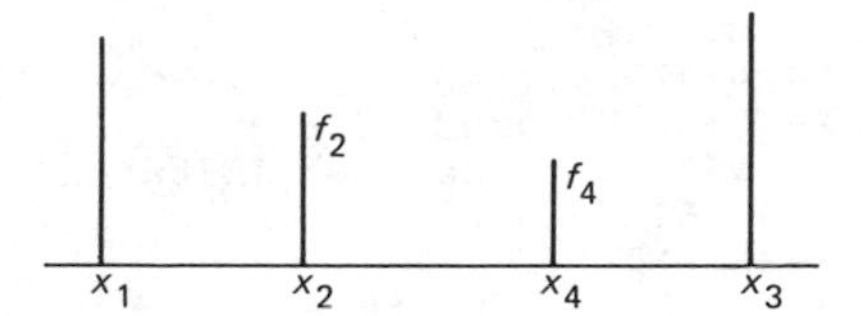

(iii) $x_4 < x_2$
$f_4 > f_2$
New interval (x_4, x_3) with x_2 included.
Line 42Ø in program

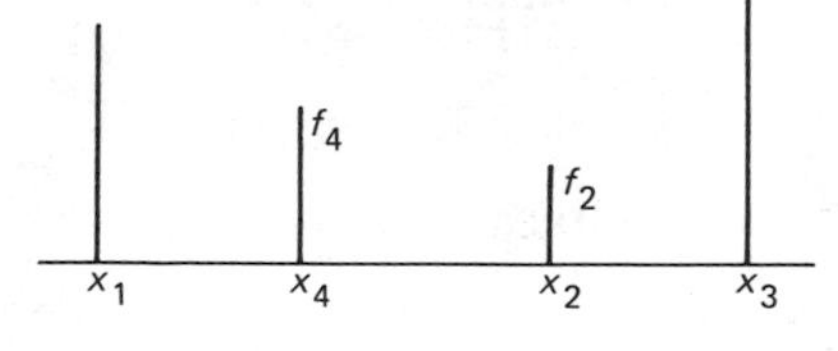

(iv) $x_4 > x_2$
$f_4 > f_2$
New interval (x_1, x_4) with x_2 included.
Line 46Ø in program

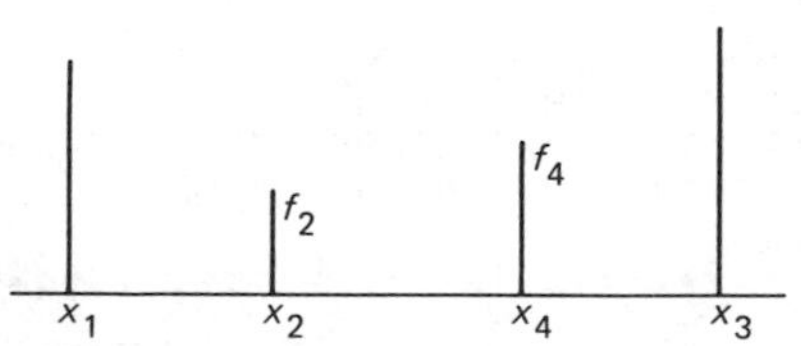

Figure 2.3

Once this first point is located we have no further use for the Fibonacci numbers. The ε we use may be dictated by practical considerations or it may be arbitrary. It needs to be less than L_1/F_{n+1} or else we are wasting function evaluations. (See Question 3 in Exercises 2.)

Thus the Fibonacci search, so called because of the natural occurrence of the Fibonacci numbers, is an iterative search routine. When we search the interval (x_1, x_3) with x_2 already in this interval we always choose our next point x_4 so that $x_3 - x_4 = x_2 - x_1$ or $x_4 - x_1 = x_3 - x_2$, i.e.,

$$x_4 = x_1 - x_2 + x_3. \tag{2.5}$$

If $f(x_2) = f_2$ and $f(x_4) = f_4$ there are four cases to consider (see Fig. 2.3).

The program given incorporates the steps indicated. We can use it as it stands with up to 40 function evaluations. The function being considered is evidently $f(x) = x^4 - 14x^3 + 60x^2 - 70x$ (see line 1ØØØ).

```
READY.

 2Ø PRINT"FIBONACCI SEARCH":PRINT"":PRINT""
 3Ø REM THIS PROGRAM SEARCHES (A,B) FOR
 4Ø REM THE MIN. POINT OF A UNIMODAL
 5Ø REM FUNCTION F(X) USING N FUNCTION
 6Ø REM EVALUATIONS.F(X) IS EVALUATED
 7Ø REM AT 1ØØØ BY Z=F(X).
 8Ø REM THE FIBONACCI NUMBERS NEEDED
 9Ø REM ARE NOW EVALUATED.
 1ØØ DIM F(4Ø)
 11Ø PRINT"SPECIFY N":INPUT N
 12Ø F(Ø)=1:F(1)=1
 13Ø FOR I=2 TO N
 14Ø F(I)=F(I-1)+F(I-2)
 15Ø NEXT I
 16Ø PRINT"SPECIFY EPSILON":INPUT E
 2ØØ PRINT"SPECIFY INTERVAL (A,B)"
 21Ø INPUT A,B
 25Ø X1=A:X2=A+((B-A)*F(N-1)+E*(-1)↑N)/F(N):X3=B
 26Ø X=X2:GOSUB 1ØØØ:F2=Z
 27Ø PRINT"          CURRENT INTERVAL"
 28Ø K=1:PRINT X1,X3
 29Ø X4=X1-X2+X3
 3ØØ X=X4:GOSUB 1ØØØ:F4=Z
 31Ø IF F4>F2 THEN GOTO 4ØØ
 32Ø IF X2<X4 THEN GOTO 36Ø
 33Ø X3=X2:X2=X4:F2=F4:PRINT X1,X3
 34Ø GOTO 5ØØ
 36Ø X1=X2:X2=X4:F2=F4:PRINT X1,X3
 37Ø GOTO 5ØØ
 4ØØ IF X2<X4 THEN GOTO 46Ø
 42Ø X1=X4:PRINT X1,X3
 43Ø GOTO 5ØØ
 46Ø X3=X4:PRINT X1,X3
 5ØØ K=K+1
 51Ø IF K<=N THEN GOTO 29Ø
 6ØØ PRINT"FINAL INTERVAL":PRINT X1,X3
 61Ø PRINT"FUNCTION VALUE",F2
 65Ø END
 1ØØØ Z=X*X*X*X-14*X*X*X+6Ø*X*X-7Ø*X
 1Ø1Ø RETURN
READY.
```

Example 1

Use Fibonacci search with 10 function evaluations to find the minimum of $f(x) = 2x^2 - e^x$ in the range (0, 1).

With ε chosen as zero the computer output appears below.

Note that the final interval of uncertainty has length

$$0{\cdot}359\,550\,563 - 0{\cdot}348\,314\,61 = 0{\cdot}011\,235\,953 \approx \tfrac{1}{89} = \frac{1}{F_{10}}.$$

With six figure accuracy the minimum is at $x^* = 0{\cdot}357\,403$ with $f(x^*) = -1{\cdot}174\,138$.

```
FIBONACCI SEARCH


SPECIFY N                          1Ø
SPECIFY EPSILON                     Ø
SPECIFY INTERVAL (A,B)              Ø,1
         CURRENT INTERVAL
 Ø                 1
 Ø                 .617977528
 .235955Ø56                .617977528
 .235955Ø56                .47191Ø113
 .325842697                .47191Ø113
 .325842697                .41573Ø338
 .325842697                .382Ø22472
 .3483146Ø6                .382Ø22472
 .3483146Ø6                .37Ø786515
 .3483146Ø6                .35955Ø563
 .34831461                .35955Ø563
FINAL INTERVAL
 .34831461                .35955Ø563
FUNCTION VALUE              -1.17413215
```

Example 2

Find the minimum of $f(x) = x^4 - 14x^3 + 60x^2 - 70x$ in the range (0, 2). Use 20 function evaluations. See Question 9 of Exercises 1.

With $z = f(x)$ at line 1ØØØ, $N = 20$, $\varepsilon = 0$, the output is given below.

```
FIBONACCI SEARCH


SPECIFY N                          2Ø
SPECIFY EPSILON                     Ø
SPECIFY INTERVAL (A,B)              Ø,2
         CURRENT INTERVAL
 Ø                 2
 Ø                 1.236Ø6797
 .47213594                1.236Ø6797
 .47213594                .944271879
 .652475789                .944271879
 .652475789                .832815638
 .721359396                .832815638
 .763932Ø3                .832815638
 .763932Ø3                .8Ø65Ø4664
 .763932Ø3                .79Ø243ØØ4
 .773981344                .79Ø243ØØ4
 .773981344                .784Ø3Ø658
 .777818311                .784Ø3Ø658
 .777818311                .781655279
```

```
 .7792799              .781655279
 .78Ø19369              .781655279
 .78Ø19369              .78110748
 .78Ø559681              .78110748
 .78Ø741489              .78110748
 .78Ø741489             .78Ø925673
 .78Ø743865             .78Ø925673
FINAL INTERVAL
 .78Ø743865             .78Ø925673
FUNCTION VALUE          -24.36960Ø15
```

2.3 Golden Section Search

It is not always possible to specify in advance how many function evaluations will be made. We need this number in Fibonacci search in order to determine L_2, the position of the first experiment (see equation 2.4).

The Golden Section search is nearly as efficient as the Fibonacci search but does not require n, the number of function evaluations, to be specified at the outset. When we have made j evaluations, then, by the same reasoning as before we have that

$$L_{j-1} = L_j + L_{j+1} \quad \text{(see equation 2.1).} \tag{2.6}$$

However, if n is not known we cannot use the condition $L_{n-1} = 2L_n - \varepsilon$. If we keep the ratio of successive intervals constant,

$$\frac{L_{j-1}}{L_j} = \frac{L_j}{L_{j+1}} = \frac{L_{j+1}}{L_{j+2}} \text{ etc.} = \tau, \tag{2.7}$$

then

$$\frac{L_{j-1}}{L_j} = 1 + \frac{L_{j+1}}{L_j},$$

i.e., $\tau = 1 + 1/\tau$.

$$\therefore \quad \tau^2 - \tau - 1 = 0 \quad \text{whence} \quad \tau = \frac{1+\sqrt{5}}{2} \approx 1{\cdot}618\,033\,989.$$

Then

$$\frac{L_{j-1}}{L_{j+1}} = \tau^2, \quad \frac{L_{j-2}}{L_{j+1}} = \tau^3 \text{ etc.}$$

$$\therefore \quad \frac{L_1}{L_n} = \tau^{n-1}.$$

$$\therefore \quad L_n = \frac{L_1}{\tau^{n-1}}. \tag{2.8}$$

The results of the two function evaluations being considered will determine which interval is to be investigated further. This interval will contain one of the previous points and the next point is placed symmetrically with respect to this. The first point is placed at a distance L_1/τ from one end, the second the same distance from the other end. Since

$$\operatorname*{Limit}_{n\to\infty} \frac{F_{n-1}}{F_n} = \frac{1}{\tau}, \quad \text{(see Question 2, Exercises 2),}$$

we see from equation 2.4 that Golden Section search is a limiting form of Fibonacci search. The name Golden Section comes from the ratio in equation 2.7. We see that L_{j-1} is divided into two parts such that the ratio of the whole to the greater part is equal to the ratio of the greater part to the smaller part, the so called Golden Ratio.

Thus if we search the interval (x_0, x_3) and have two function values f_1 and f_2 at x_1 and x_2 we have two cases to consider (see Fig. 2.4).

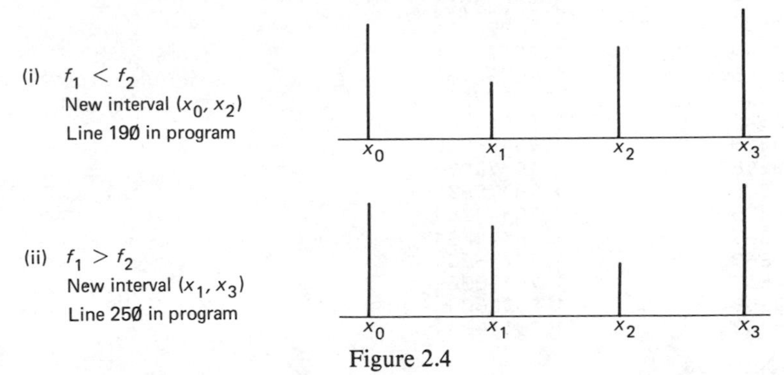

Figure 2.4

The following program implements the Golden Section search. The accuracy given can of course be varied by the choice of value at line 3ØØ. When applied to the function $f(x) = -e^{-x} \ln(x)$ the output is given below. The interval searched is (0, 2).

The true minimum is at 1·763 222 11 with function value −0·097 260 131 3.

```
READY.

 1Ø PRINT"          GOLDSEARCH":PRINT"":PRINT""
 2Ø REM THIS PROGRAM WILL SEARCH THE
 3Ø REM INTERVAL (A,B) FOR THE MINIMUM
 4Ø REM POINT OF A UNIMODAL FUNCTION F(X).
 5Ø REM THE FINAL VALUE OF X IS CORRECT TO 4D.
 6Ø REM SPECIFY F(X) AT 1ØØØ BY Z=..
 9Ø PRINT"SPECIFY INTERVAL (A,B)":INPUT A,B
 1ØØ T1=Ø.381966Ø113:T2=1-T1
 11Ø XØ=A:X1=A+T1*(B-A):X2=A+T2*(B-A):X3=B
 12Ø X=X1:GOSUB 1ØØØ:F1=Z
 14Ø X=X2:GOSUB 1ØØØ:F2=Z
 15Ø PRINT"          CURRENT INTERVAL"
 17Ø PRINTXØ,X3
 18Ø IF F2<F1 THEN GOTO 25Ø
 19Ø I=X2-XØ:X3=X2:X2=X1:X1=XØ+T1*I
 2ØØ F2=F1:X=X1:GOSUB 1ØØØ
 21Ø F1=Z:GOTO 3ØØ
 25Ø I=X3-X1:XØ=X1:X1=X2:X2=XØ+T2*I
 26Ø F1=F2:X=X2:GOSUB 1ØØØ:F2=Z
 3ØØ IF I>Ø.ØØØØ5 THEN GOTO 17Ø
 45Ø PRINT
 46Ø PRINT"FINAL SOLUTION"
 47Ø PRINT "X="X1,"F(X)="F1
 5ØØ END
 1ØØØ Z=-EXP(-X)*LOG(X)
 1Ø1Ø RETURN
READY.
```

```
          GOLDSEARCH


SPECIFY INTERVAL (A,B)    Ø,2
        CURRENT INTERVAL
 Ø           2
 .763932Ø22             2
 1.236Ø6798             2
 1.527864Ø5             2
 1.7Ø82Ø393             2
 1.7Ø82Ø393             1.88854382
 1.7Ø82Ø393             1.819660Ø11
 1.7Ø82Ø393             1.777Ø8764
 1.73451517             1.777Ø8764
 1.75Ø77641             1.777Ø8764
 1.75Ø77641             1.767Ø3764
 1.75698765             1.767Ø3764
 1.76Ø8264             1.767Ø3764
 1.76Ø8264             1.76466516
 1.76229268             1.76466516
 1.76229268             1.76375895
 1.76285275             1.76375895
 1.76285275             1.76341281
 1.763Ø6667             1.76341281
 1.763Ø6667             1.763280Ø6
 1.76314839             1.763280Ø6
 1.76319889             1.763280Ø6
 1.76319889             1.76324939

FINAL SOLUTION
X= 1.763210Ø81              F(X)=-.Ø97260Ø1313
```

2.4 The Curve Fitting Approach

In the previous two sections, we tried to determine a *small* interval in which the minimum of the function was located. In the next two sections a different approach is adopted. We use a few function values, at particular points, in order to approximate the function by a simple polynomial, at least over a limited range of values. We then approximate the position of the function minimum by the position of the polynomial's minimum. The latter is easy to calculate.

2.5 Quadratic Interpolation

If we know the values of a function $f(x)$ at three distinct points α, β, γ to be f_α, f_β, f_γ respectively, then we can approximate $f(x)$ by the quadratic function

$$\phi(x) = Ax^2 + Bx + C \tag{2.9}$$

where A, B and C are determined by the equations

$$\begin{aligned} A\alpha^2 + B\alpha + C &= f_\alpha \\ A\beta^2 + B\beta + C &= f_\beta. \\ A\gamma^2 + B\gamma + C &= f_\gamma \end{aligned} \tag{2.10}$$

The equations give

$$
\begin{aligned}
A &= [(\gamma-\beta)\, f_\alpha + (\alpha-\gamma)\, f_\beta + (\beta-\alpha)\, f_\gamma]/\Delta \\
B &= [(\beta^2-\gamma^2)\, f_\alpha + (\gamma^2-\alpha^2)\, f_\beta + (\alpha^2-\beta^2)\, f_\gamma]/\Delta \\
C &= [\beta\gamma(\gamma-\beta)\, f_\alpha + \gamma\alpha(\alpha-\gamma)\, f_\beta + \alpha\beta(\beta-\alpha)\, f_\gamma]/\Delta
\end{aligned}
\tag{2.11}
$$

where $\Delta = (\alpha-\beta)(\beta-\gamma)(\gamma-\alpha)$. Clearly $\phi(x)$ will have a minimum at $x = -B/2A$ if $A > 0$. Thus we approximate the position of the minimum of $f(x)$ by

$$
\delta = \frac{1}{2}\left[\frac{(\beta^2-\gamma^2)\, f_\alpha + (\gamma^2-\alpha^2)\, f_\beta + (\alpha^2-\beta^2)\, f_\gamma}{(\beta-\gamma)\, f_\alpha + (\gamma-\alpha)\, f_\beta + (\alpha-\beta)\, f_\gamma}\right]
\tag{2.12}
$$

The method can be used in its own right for a function of one variable. It can be very useful for carrying out the linear search required in the procedures of Chapter 4. In these cases we wish to find the minimum of $f(\mathbf{x})$ at points on the line $\mathbf{x}_0 + \lambda\mathbf{d}$, where $\mathbf{x}_0$ is a given point, and $\mathbf{d}$ specifies a given direction. The values of $f(\mathbf{x}_0 + \lambda\mathbf{d})$ on this line are functions of the one variable λ,

$$
\phi(\lambda) = f(\mathbf{x}_0 + \lambda\mathbf{d}).
\tag{2.13}
$$

The ideas and results above are transformed into a computational procedure as follows. We assume that we have a unimodal function $f(x)$ of one variable, an initial approximation to the position of its minimum, and a step length H, which is the same order of magnitude as the true minimum x^* is from A (not always easy conditions to satisfy). The steps in the procedure are as follows:

(i) Calculate $f(A)$ and $f(A + H)$.

(ii) If $f(A) < f(A + H)$ take the third point as $A - H$ and find $f(A - H)$. Otherwise take the third point as $A + 2H$ and find $f(A + 2H)$ (see Fig. 2.5).

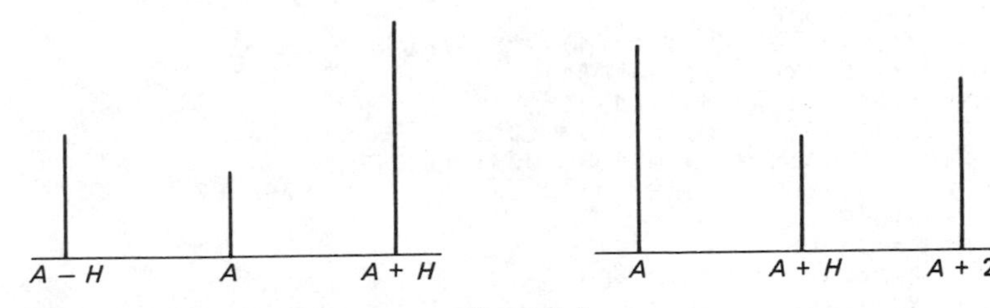

Figure 2.5

(iii) Use the three points to find δ from equation 2.12 and evaluate $f(\delta)$.

(iv) If the difference between the positions of the lowest function value and the next lowest function value is less than the required accuracy terminate the process.

(v) If we do not terminate at stage (iv) we would normally discard the point with the highest function value and then return to step (iii). If however by retaining the point with the highest function value we put a definite bracket on the location of the minimum, then we should indeed retain this value and then return to step (iii). See Fig. 2.6 in which we would retain x_1, x_2 and x_4 rather than x_1, x_2, x_3.

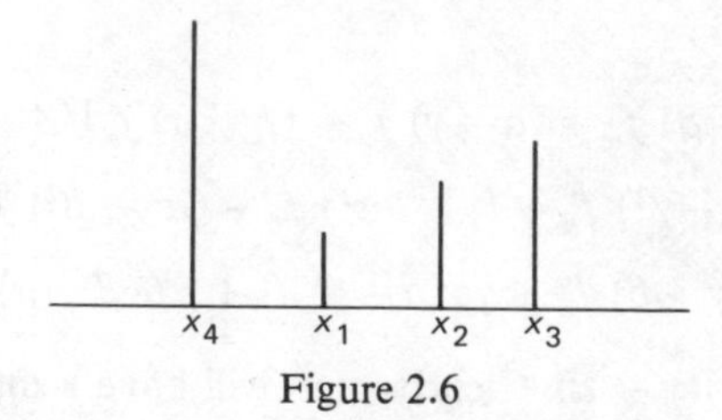

Figure 2.6

The program listed implements this procedure. Note that if the accuracy E is set too small α, β, γ and f_α, f_β, f_γ will be very close together and δ (equation 2.12) may well become totally unreliable. To overcome this problem equation 2.12 is rewritten as

$$\delta = \tfrac{1}{2}(\alpha + \beta) + \frac{\tfrac{1}{2}(f_\alpha - f_\beta)(\beta - \gamma)(\gamma - \alpha)}{(\beta - \gamma)\, f_\alpha + (\gamma - \alpha)\, f_\beta + (\alpha - \beta)\, f_\gamma} \tag{2.14}$$

in the second and subsequent interpolations.

```
READY.

 10 PRINT"QUADRATIC INTERPOLATION"
 20 REM THIS PROGRAM USES POWELL'S QUADRATIC INTERPOLATION
 30 REM PROCEDURE TO FIND'THE MINIMUM OF A FUNCTION F(X)
 40 REM EVALUATED BY Z=F(X). AT SUB. 1000
 100 PRINT"SPECIFY INITIAL VALUE":INPUT A
 110 PRINT"SPECIFY STEP H":INPUT H
 150 PRINT"SPECIFY ACCURACY E":INPUT E
 190 REM INITIATE PROCESS WITH FIRST THREE POINTS
 200 DIM X(4),F(4)
 210 X(1)=A:X=X(1):GOSUB 1000:F(1)=Z
 220 X(2)=A+H:X=X(2):GOSUB 1000:F(2)=Z
 230 IF F(1)<F(2) THEN X(3)=A-H:X=X(3):GOSUB 1000:F(3)=Z:GOTO 250
 240 X(3)=A+2*H:X=X(3):GOSUB 1000:F(3)=Z
 250 PRINT"       CURRENT VALUES"
 260 PRINT"     X(I)           F(I)"
 270 REM CALCULATE FIRST FITTED MINIMUM IN LINES 300-350
 300 DN=(X(2)-X(3))*F(1)
 310 DN=DN+(X(3)-X(1))*F(2)+(X(1)-X(2))*F(3)
 320 NM=(X(2)*X(2)-X(3)*X(3))*F(1)
 330 NM=NM+(X(3)*X(3)-X(1)*X(1))*F(2)
 340 NM=NM+(X(1)*X(1)-X(2)*X(2))*F(3)
 350 X(4)=NM/(2*DN):X=X(4):GOSUB 1000:F(4)=Z
 380 REM PUT FUNCTION VALUES IN ORDER IN LINES 400-460
 400 FOR J=1 TO 3
 410 FOR K=J+1 TO 4
 420 IF F(J)<=F(K) THEN GOTO 460
 430 X=X(J):X(J)=X(K):X(K)=X
 440 F=F(J):F(J)=F(K):F(K)=F
 450 REM SWOPS F(J)&F(K) AND X(J)&X(K) IF IN WRONG ORDER
 460 NEXT K:NEXT J
 470 FOR I=1 TO 4:PRINT X(I),F(I):NEXT I
 480 PRINT"":PRINT""
 490 REM FINISH IF ACCURACY IS O.K.
 500 IF ABS(X(1)-X(2))<E THEN GOTO 800
 510 REM RETAIN BEST THREE POINTS
 520 S1=SGN(X(2)-X(1)):S2=SGN(X(3)-X(1))
 530 S3=SGN(X(4)-X(1))
 540 IF S1=S2 AND S1=-S4 THEN X(3)=X(4):F(3)=F(4)
 550 REM SECOND INTERPOLATION
 560 DN=(X(2)-X(3))*F(1)+(X(3)-X(1))*F(2)+(X(1)-X(2))*F(3)
 570 F=(F(1)-F(2))/(2*DN)
```

```
 580 F=F*(X(2)-X(3))*(X(3)-X(1))
 590 X(4)=(X(1)+X(2))/2+F
 600 X=X(4):GOSUB 1000:F(4)=Z
 610 REM REPEAT SECOND INTERPOLATION
 620 GOTO 400
 800 PRINT"      FINAL SOLUTION      "
 810 PRINT"X="X(1),"F="F(1)
 850 END
 1000 Z=2*X*X-EXP(X)
 1010 RETURN
READY.
```

Example 1

Use quadratic interpolation to find the position of the minimum of $z = 2x^2 - e^x$ to an accuracy of 0·0001. Use 1 as the initial value A and take $H = 0{\cdot}5$.

The computer output appears below.

```
QUADRATIC INTERPOLATION
SPECIFY INITIAL VALUE    1
SPECIFY STEP H           0.5
SPECIFY ACCURACY E       0.0001
       CURRENT VALUES
    X(I)              F(I)
 .5             -1.14872127
 .0470197921             -1.04372103
 1             -.718281828
 1.5              .0183109295


 .37459168             -1.17375958
 .5             -1.14872127
 .0470197921             -1.04372103
 1             -.718281828


 .36150412             -1.17411648
 .37459168             -1.17375958
 .5             -1.14872127
 .0470197921             -1.04372103


 .357093342              -1.17413796
 .36150412             -1.17411648
 .37459168             -1.17375958
 .5             -1.14872127


 .357396971              -1.17413808
 .357093342              -1.17413796
 .36150412             -1.17411648
 .37459168             -1.17375958


 .357396971              -1.17413808
 .357402799              -1.17413808
 .357093342              -1.17413796
 .36150412             -1.17411648


     FINAL SOLUTION
X= .357396971             F=-1.17413808
```

2.6 Cubic Interpolation

The quadratic interpolation of the previous section, often called Powell's method, approximated the function by a quadratic. Davidon's method of the present section is more accurate and approximates the function by a cubic polynomial. It uses the values of the function and its gradient at two points in order to fit the cubic. It is widely used in the context of linear searches in Chapter 4, and we shall treat it from this point of view.

Thus we consider the problem of minimising $f(\mathbf{x})$ at points on the line $\mathbf{x}_0 + h\mathbf{d}$, i.e. of minimising

$$\begin{aligned}\phi(h) &= f(\mathbf{x}_0 + h\mathbf{d}) \\ &= f(x_{01} + hd_1, x_{02} + hd_2, \ldots, x_{0n} + hd_n). \end{aligned} \tag{2.15}$$

$$\frac{d\phi}{dh} = \frac{\partial f}{\partial x_1}(\mathbf{x}_0 + h\mathbf{d})\, d_1 + \frac{\partial f}{\partial x_2}(\mathbf{x}_0 + h\mathbf{d})\, d_2 + \cdots + \frac{\partial f}{\partial x_n}(\mathbf{x}_0 + h\mathbf{d})\, d_n.$$

$$\therefore \quad \frac{d\phi}{dh} = \nabla f(\mathbf{x}_0 + h\mathbf{d})^{\mathrm{T}}\, \mathbf{d} = \mathbf{g}(\mathbf{x}_0 + h\mathbf{d})^{\mathrm{T}}\, \mathbf{d}. \tag{2.16}$$

We suppose that we know the values of

$$\begin{aligned} &\phi(p) = \phi_p, \quad \phi(q) = \phi_q \\ &\frac{d\phi}{dh}(p) = G_p, \quad \frac{d\phi}{dh}(q) = G_q. \end{aligned} \tag{2.17}$$

We can use this information to fit a cubic polynomial

$$a + bh + ch^2 + dh^3 \tag{2.18}$$

which will approximate $\phi(h)$. If $p = 0$, the equations determining a, b, c, d are

$$\begin{aligned} a \qquad\qquad\quad &= \phi_p \\ a + bq + cq^2 + dq^3 &= \phi_q \\ b \qquad\qquad\quad &= G_p \\ b + 2cq + 3dq^2 &= G_q \end{aligned} \tag{2.19}$$

with solution

$$a = \phi_p, \quad b = G_p, \quad c = -\frac{(G_p + z)}{q}, \quad d = \frac{G_p + G_q + 2z}{3q^2} \tag{2.20}$$

where

$$z = \frac{3(\phi_p - \phi_q)}{q} + G_p + G_q.$$

The turning points of the fitted cubic are the solutions of

$$G_p - 2(G_p + z)\frac{h}{q} + (G_p + G_q + 2z)\left(\frac{h}{q}\right)^2 = 0.$$

Thus if r is the position of the minimum of the fitted cubic

$$\frac{r}{q}=\frac{(G_p+z)\pm[(G_p+z)^2-G_p(G_p+G_q+2z)]^{1/2}}{G_p+G_q+2z}=\frac{G_p+z\pm w}{G_p+G_q+2z}, \qquad (2.21)$$

where

$$w=(z^2-G_pG_q)^{1/2}. \qquad (2.22)$$

One of these corresponds to the minimum. The second derivative is

$$2c+6dh. \qquad (2.23)$$

If we take the positive sign, with

$$\frac{h}{q}=\frac{G_p+z+w}{G_p+G_q+2z}$$

the second derivative has the value

$$-\frac{2(G_p+z)}{q}+\frac{2(G_p+G_q+2z)}{q^2}\cdot\frac{q(G_p+z+w)}{(G_p+G_q+2z)}$$

$$=\frac{1}{q}(-2G_p-2z+2G_p+2z+2w)=\frac{2w}{q}>0.$$

Thus

$$\frac{r}{q}=\frac{G_p+z+w}{G_p+G_q+2z}. \qquad (2.24)$$

Better numerical results are obtained from the equivalent formula

$$\frac{r}{q}=1-\frac{G_q+w-z}{G_q-G_p+2w}=\frac{z+w-G_p}{G_q-G_p+2w}. \qquad (2.25)$$

It is left as an exercise to show that equations 2.24 and 2.25 are equivalent.

The choice of q is at our discretion. If $G_p<0$ we would take q to be positive, i.e. take a step in the direction of decreasing $\phi(h)$, otherwise we would take q to be negative. The magnitude of q is such that the interval $(0, q)$ includes the minimum. This will be so if $\phi_q>\phi_p$ (Fig. 2.7(i)) or if $G_q>0$ (Fig. 2.7(ii)).

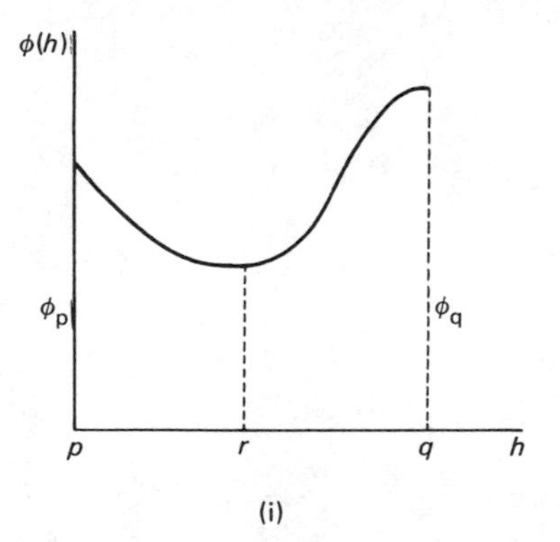

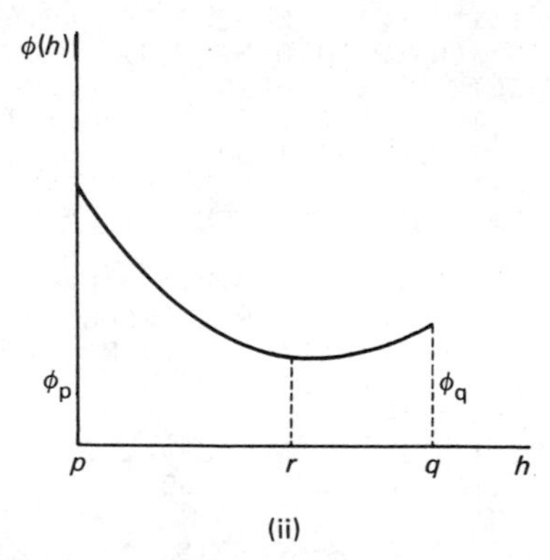

Figure 2.7

When neither of these conditions is satisfied we double the value of q, repeatedly if necessary, until our interval does bracket a minimum.

The problem of finding an initial value for q remains. There are real difficulties in finding a value that will be satisfactory for *all* problems. Davidon and Fletcher and Powell suggest

$$q = \min\{\eta, -2(\phi_p - \phi_m)/G_p\} \tag{2.26}$$

where ϕ_m is an estimate, preferably on the low side of the true minimum of $\phi(h)$, and η is a constant, usually taken to be 2 or 1.

The steps in the iterative procedure are thus

(i) Find $\phi_p = f(\mathbf{x}_0)$ and $G_p = [\mathbf{g}(\mathbf{x}_0)]^T \mathbf{d}$.

(ii) Check that $G_p < 0$ and if not search along $-\mathbf{d}$. Choose q from equation 2.26. We just have to 'guess' for ϕ_m.

(iii) Evaluate $\phi_q = f(\mathbf{x}_0 + q\mathbf{d})$ and $G_q = [\mathbf{g}(\mathbf{x}_0 + q\mathbf{d})]^T \mathbf{d}$.

(iv) If $G_q > 0$ or $\phi_q > \phi_p$ we have bracketed the minimum. If not replace q by $2q$ and return to step (iii).

(v) Use equation 2.25 to approximate the minimum by r in $(0, q)$.

(vi) Stop if $|d\phi/dh| = |[\mathbf{g}(\mathbf{x}_0 + r\mathbf{d})]^T \mathbf{d}| = |G_r| < \varepsilon$ where ε is some specified accuracy.

(vii) Return to step (v) using the interval $(0, r)$ if $G_r > 0$, or, the interval (r, q) if $G_r \leqslant 0$.

The stopping condition at (vi) tests the derivative. Previous tests have stopped when the position of the minimum has shown no real movement. It might be noted that in general it is easier to find the minimum of the function than the position of the minimum. The latter is determined with less accuracy.

The algorithm just described is implemented in the following program.

```
READY.

 20 PRINT"CUBIC INTERPOLATION"
 30 REM THIS PROGRAM FINDS THE MINIMUM OF F(X+LAM*D)
 40 REM ALONG THE LINE X+LAM*D. F(X1,X2,..) IS EVALUATED AT
 50 REM SUB. 5000 BY Z=F(X1,X2,..,XN).THE GRADIENT VECTOR
 60 REM OF F(X) IS EVALUATED AT SUB. 6000;G(1),G(2),..,G(N)
 100 PRINT"SPECIFY NUMBER OF VARIABLES":INPUT N
 120 DIM X(N),P(N),Q(N),D(N)
 150 PRINT"INITIAL POINT"
 160 FOR I= 1 TO N:INPUT X(I):NEXT I
 200 PRINT"DIRECTION D"
 220 FOR I=1 TO N:INPUT D(I):NEXT I
 300 PRINT" SPECIFY ACCURACY E"
 310 INPUT E
 350 PRINT"GUESSED MINIMUM":INPUT FM
 400 PRINT"         CURRENT VALUES"
 410 FOR I=1 TO N:P(I)=X(I):PRINT"X";I,X(I):NEXT I
 500 REM FIRST POINT P
 510 GOSUB 5000
 520 PRINT"ITERATION";CC"VALUE";Z
 530 FP=Z:GOSUB 6000:G1=G0
 600 GP=0
 610 FOR I=1 TO N:GP=GP+G(I)*D(I):NEXT I
 620 IF GP<=0 THEN GOTO 680
 625 REM FIND INITIAL STEP AND IF NECESSARY
```

```
626 REM REVERSE DIRECTION TO GO DOWNHILL
630 QX=ABS(2*(FP-FM)/GP):IF QX>1 THEN QX=1
640 FOR I=1 TO N
650 X(I)=P(I)-QX*D(I):P(I)=X(I):NEXT I
660 GOSUB 5000:FP=Z:PRINT"INSTABILITY?"
670 GOSUB 6000:G1=G0:GOTO 600
680 QX=ABS(2*(FP-FM)/GP):IF QX>1 THEN QX=1
690 HH=QX
700 REM FIND NEXT POINT Q
710 BB=HH
720 FOR I=1 TO N
730 Q(I)=P(I)+BB*D(I):X(I)=Q(I)
740 NEXT I
750 GOSUB 5000:FQ=Z
760 GOSUB 6000:G2=G0
770 GQ=0
780 FOR I=1 TO N
790 GQ=GQ+G(I)*D(I)
800 NEXT I
810 IF GQ>0 OR FQ>FP THEN GOTO 830
815 REM DO CUBIC INTERPOLATION OR DOUBLE STEP TO BRACKET MINIMUM
820 HH=2*HH:GOTO 700
830 ZZ=3*(FP-FQ)/HH:ZZ=ZZ+GP+GQ
840 WW=ZZ*ZZ-GP*GQ:IF WW<0 THEN WW=0
850 W=SQR(WW)
860 DD=HH*(1-(GQ+W-ZZ)/(GQ-GP+2*W))
870 FOR I=1 TO N:X(I)=P(I)+DD*D(I):NEXT I
880 GOSUB 5000:FR=Z
890 GOSUB 6000:G3=G0
895 REM FIND GRADIENT AT NEW POINT
900 GR=0
910 FOR I=1 TO N:GR=GR+G(I)*D(I):NEXT I
920 IF GR>0 THEN GOTO 1000
925 REM FIND NEW INTERVAL AND CHECK FOR FINISH
930 IF ABS(GR)<E THEN GOTO 1300
940 HH=BB-DD
950 FOR I=1 TO N:P(I)=X(I):PRINT"X";I,X(I):NEXT I
960 CC=CC+1:PRINT"ITERATION"CC"VALUE"Z
970 FP=Z:GP=GR:G1=G0:GOTO 830
1000 IF ABS(GR)<E THEN GOTO 1300
1005 REM WE REPEAT THE CUBIC INTERP. ON THE
1006 REM NEW INTERVAL BB-DD, 940, OR DD, 1010
1010 HH=DD
1020 FOR I=1 TO N:Q(I)=X(I):PRINT"X";I,X(I):NEXT I
1030 CC=CC+1:PRINT"ITERATION"CC"VALUE"Z
1040 FQ=Z:GQ=GR:G2=G0:GOTO 830
1300 PRINT"MINIMISATION COMPLETE"
1310 PRINT"ITERATIONS="CC"VALUE="Z
1320 FOR I=1 TO N
1330 PRINT "X";I,X(I)
1340 NEXT I
1350 END
5000 Z=0
5010 Z=100*(X(2)-X(1)*X(1))↑2
5020 Z=Z+(1-X(1))↑2
5100 TT=TT+1
5200 RETURN
6000 G0=0
6100 G(1)=-400*X(1)*(X(2)-X(1)*X(1))
6110 G(1)=G(1)-2*(1-X(1))
6200 G(2)=200*(X(2)-X(1)*X(1))
7000 FOR I=1 TO N:G0=G0+G(I)*G(I):NEXT I
7010 G0=SQR(G0)
7500 RETURN
READY.
```

Example 1

Find the minimum of $f(x_1, x_2) = 100(x_2 - x_1^2)^2 + (1 - x_1)^2$ along the line through $(-1, 0)$ in the direction $(5, 1)$.

As listed the subroutines 5ØØØ and 6ØØØ are appropriate. The accuracy E used was 0·0001 and ϕ_m was taken to be zero. The output given is now listed.

```
CUBIC INTERPOLATION
SPECIFY NUMBER OF VARIABLES   2
INITIAL POINT                -1, Ø
DIRECTION D                   5, 1
 SPECIFY ACCURACY E           Ø.ØØØ1
GUESSED MINIMUM               Ø
       CURRENT VALUES
X 1            -1
X 2             Ø
ITERATION Ø VALUE 1Ø4
X 1            -.399424711
X 2             .12Ø115Ø58
ITERATION 1 VALUE 2.11382292
X 1            -.336511454
X 2             .1326977Ø9
ITERATION 2 VALUE 1.82412327
X 1            -.341386326
X 2             .131722735
ITERATION 3 VALUE 1.82235478
X 1             .242295328
X 2             .248459Ø66
ITERATION 4 VALUE 4.1747ØØØ3
X 1             .58132Ø727
X 2             .316264145
ITERATION 5 VALUE .222249674
X 1             .561168758
X 2             .312233752
ITERATION 6 VALUE .19328929
X 1             .9545782Ø2
X 2             .39Ø915641
ITERATION 7 VALUE 27.Ø736784
X 1             .563828219
X 2             .312765644
ITERATION 8 VALUE .1928843Ø6
MINIMISATION COMPLETE
ITERATIONS= 8 VALUE= .192865822
X 1             .563369687
X 2             .312673937
```

2.7 References

1 W. C. Davidon, 'Variable metric method for minimisation', *AEC R & D Report*, ANL-5990, Argonne National Laboratory, 1959.

2 R. Fletcher and M. J. D. Powell, 'A rapidly convergent descent method for minimisation', *The Comp Journal*, **6**, 163–168, 1963.

3 J. Kiefer, 'Sequential minimax search for a maximum', *Proc. Am. Math. Soc.*, **4**, 502–506, 1953.

4 M. J. D. Powell, 'An efficient method of finding the minimum of a function of several variables without calculating derivatives', *The Comp. Journal*, **7**, 155–162, 1964

Exercises 2

1 If $F_0 = 1$ and $F_1 = 1$ and $F_k = F_{k-1} + F_{k-2}$ for $k \geqslant 2$ show that

$$F_n = \frac{\tau^{n+1} - (-\tau)^{-(n+1)}}{\sqrt{5}} \quad \text{where } \tau = \frac{1+\sqrt{5}}{2} \approx 1{\cdot}618\,033\,989.$$

Show by using the recurrence that $F_2 = 2$, $F_3 = 3$, $F_4 = 5$, $F_5 = 8$, $F_6 = 13$, ..., $F_{10} = 89$, ... etc. ... $F_{19} = 6765$, $F_{20} = 10\,946$.

2 Show that

(i) $F_{n-1}F_{n-2} - F_nF_{n-3} = (-1)^n$. [See equation 2.4.]
(ii) $F_n \approx \tau^{n+1}/\sqrt{5}$ for large n.
(iii) $F_{n-1}/F_n \approx 1/\tau$ for large n.

3 If we have to separate our points by at least ε, 2ε will be the smallest practical interval of uncertainty; thus $L_n \geqslant 2\varepsilon$ sets a bound on n, the number of useful experiments. Show that this leads to

$$\varepsilon < L_1/F_{n+1}.$$

4 Show that in order to reduce the interval of uncertainty to 1% of its original value, we need 11 function evaluations with Fibonacci search. If we choose the positions of all the points at the outset what is the minimum number of points needed? [Don't gamble on getting favourable outcomes.]

5 Use Fibonacci search with 10 function evaluations to locate the minimum of $2x^2 + 3\,\mathrm{e}^{-x}$ in the interval (0, 1).

6 Use Fibonacci search to locate the minimum of $x^4 - 14x^3 + 60x^2 - 70x$ within the interval (5, 7) with an accuracy of 0·01. How many function evaluations are needed?

7 Use Golden search to find the minimum of $2x^2 + 3\,\mathrm{e}^{-x}$ correct to 2 decimal places. Use (0, 1) as the original interval of uncertainty. How many function evaluations are needed? C.f. Question 5.

8 If $\alpha = 0$, $\beta = t$, $\gamma = 2t$ show that δ (equation 2.12) is given by

$$\delta = \frac{4f_\beta - 3f_\alpha - f_\gamma}{4f_\beta - 2f_\alpha - 2f_\gamma} \cdot t$$

and that this gives a minimum if $f_\alpha + f_\gamma > 2f_\beta$.

9 Use quadratic interpolation to find the position of the minimum of $-\mathrm{e}^{-x}\ln(x)$ within the interval (1, 3) to an accuracy of 0·001. [Make sure you don't use negative x values or you will get an execution error.]

10 Use quadratic interpolation to find the minium of $f(x_1, x_2) = x_1^2 + 3x_2^2 + 2x_1x_2$ along the line $\boldsymbol{\alpha} + \lambda\mathbf{d}$ where $\boldsymbol{\alpha} = \begin{pmatrix}1\\1\end{pmatrix}$ and $\mathbf{d} = \begin{pmatrix}2\\3\end{pmatrix}$, correct to 2 decimal places.

11 Verify the correctness of equations 2.11, 2.12 and 2.14.

12 Verify the correctness of equation 2.20.

13 Verify the equivalence of equations 2.24 and 2.25.

14 For the curve $y = ax^2$ show that the tangent at (x', y') meets the x-axis at $x'/2$. Hence or otherwise attempt to give the argument underlying equation 2.26.

15 Solve the equation $e^x \sin x = 1$. Try to minimise the function $f(x) = (1 - e^x \sin x)^2$.

3
Direct Search Methods—Functions of *n* Variables

3.1 Preliminary Discussion

Much effort has been devoted to devising direct search methods to locate the minimum of a function of n variables. A direct search method is one that uses function values only. A number of methods have been suggested. We shall only consider two in any detail. They are, however, two methods that experience has shown are very robust and capable of wide application.

Consider a function of two variables. Its contour lines are shown in Fig. 3.1. Its minimum is at (x_1^*, x_2^*). The crudest search method is the alternating variable search method. We start at some point A and search in the direction of the x_1-axis for the minimum in this direction and thus find B at which the tangent to the contour is parallel to the x_1-axis. From B we then search in the direction of the x_2-axis and so proceed to C and then to D by searching parallel to the x_1-axis etc. In this way we proceed to the optimum point. Any of the univariate techniques of the previous chapter could be used for the searches. It is clearly possible to extend the idea to functions of n variables.

In theory the method is reasonable if there is just one minimum. In practice it is generally too slow. Hence more sophisticated methods, which make more use of the information in the function values already obtained, have been devised.

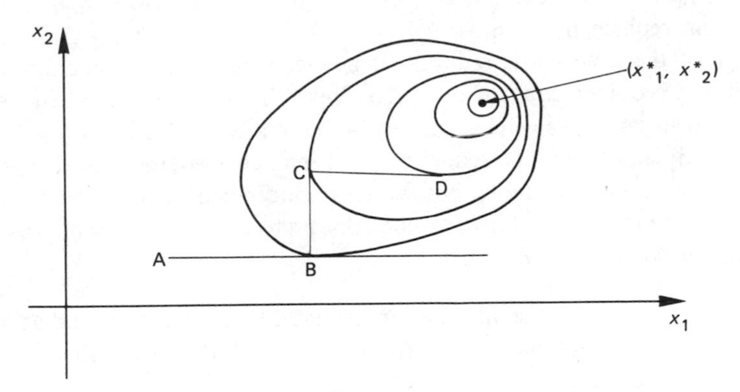

Figure 3.1

A number of functions have been constructed which because of their nature provide severe tests for such methods. A few examples are given. Rosenbrock's function:

$$f(x_1, x_2) = 100(x_2 - x_1^2)^2 + (1 - x_1)^2; \quad \mathbf{x}^* = (1, 1). \tag{3.1}$$

Powell's function:

$$f(\mathbf{x}) = (x_1 + 10x_2)^2 + 5(x_3 - x_4)^2 + (x_2 - 2x_3)^4 + 10(x_1 - x_4)^4 \quad \text{with } \mathbf{x}^* = (0, 0, 0, 0). \tag{3.2}$$

The two dimensional exponential function:

$$f(x_1, x_2) = \sum_a [(e^{-ax_1} - e^{-ax_2}) - (e^{-a} - e^{-10a})]^2 \quad \text{where } a = 0{\cdot}1(0{\cdot}1)1;\ \mathbf{x}^* = (1, 10). \tag{3.3}$$

Any optimisation procedure worthy of serious consideration should be able to handle these test problems (and others) efficiently.

3.2 The Method of Hooke and Jeeves

This method dates back to 1961 but is none the less a very efficient and ingenious procedure. The search consists of a sequence of *exploration steps* about a *base point* which if successful are followed by *pattern moves*.

The procedure is as follows.

(A) Choose an initial base point $\mathbf{b}_1$ and a step length h_j for each variable x_j; $j = 1, 2, \ldots, n$. The program given later uses a fixed step h for each variable, but the modification indicated can be useful.

(B) Carry out an exploration about $\mathbf{b}_1$. The purpose of this is to acquire knowledge about the local behaviour of the function. This knowledge is used to find a likely direction for the *pattern move* by which it is hoped to obtain an even greater reduction in the value of the function. The exploration about $\mathbf{b}_1$ proceeds as indicated.

(i) Evaluate $f(\mathbf{b}_1)$.

(ii) Each variable is now changed in turn, by adding the step length. Thus we evaluate $f(\mathbf{b}_1 + h_1\mathbf{e}_1)$ where $\mathbf{e}_1$ is a unit vector in the direction of the x_1-axis. If this reduces the function replace $\mathbf{b}_1$ by $\mathbf{b}_1 + h_1\mathbf{e}_1$. If not find $f(\mathbf{b}_1 - h_1\mathbf{e}_1)$ and replace $\mathbf{b}_1$ by $\mathbf{b}_1 - h_1\mathbf{e}_1$ if the function is reduced. If neither step gives a reduction leave $\mathbf{b}_1$ unchanged and consider changes in x_2, i.e. find $f(\mathbf{b}_1 + h_2\mathbf{e}_2)$ etc. When we have considered all n variables we will have a new base point $\mathbf{b}_2$.

(iii) If $\mathbf{b}_2 = \mathbf{b}_1$ i.e. no function reduction has been achieved, the exploration is repeated about the same base point $\mathbf{b}_1$ but with a reduced step length. Reducing the step length(s) to one tenth of its former value appears to be satisfactory in practice.

(iv) If $\mathbf{b}_2 \neq \mathbf{b}_1$ we make a *pattern move*.

(C) Pattern moves utilise the information acquired by exploration, and accomplish the function minimisation by moving in the direction of the established 'pattern'. The procedure is as follows.

(i) It seems sensible to move further from the base point $\mathbf{b}_2$ in the direction $\mathbf{b}_2 - \mathbf{b}_1$ since that move has already led to a reduction in the function value. So we evaluate the function at the next pattern point

$$\mathbf{P}_1 = \mathbf{b}_1 + 2(\mathbf{b}_2 - \mathbf{b}_1). \tag{3.4}$$

In general

$$\mathbf{P}_i = \mathbf{b}_i + 2(\mathbf{b}_{i+1} - \mathbf{b}_i). \tag{3.5}$$

(ii) Then continue with exploratory moves about $\mathbf{P}_1(\mathbf{P}_i)$.
(iii) If the lowest value at step C(ii) is less than the value at the base point $\mathbf{b}_2$ ($\mathbf{b}_{i+1}$ in general) then a new base point $\mathbf{b}_3$ ($\mathbf{b}_{i+2}$) has been reached. In this case repeat C(i). Otherwise abandon the pattern move from $\mathbf{b}_2$ ($\mathbf{b}_{i+1}$) and continue with an exploration about $\mathbf{b}_2$ ($\mathbf{b}_{i+1}$).

(D) Terminate the process when the step length(s) has been reduced to a predetermined small value.

We can give a flow chart representation of the method.

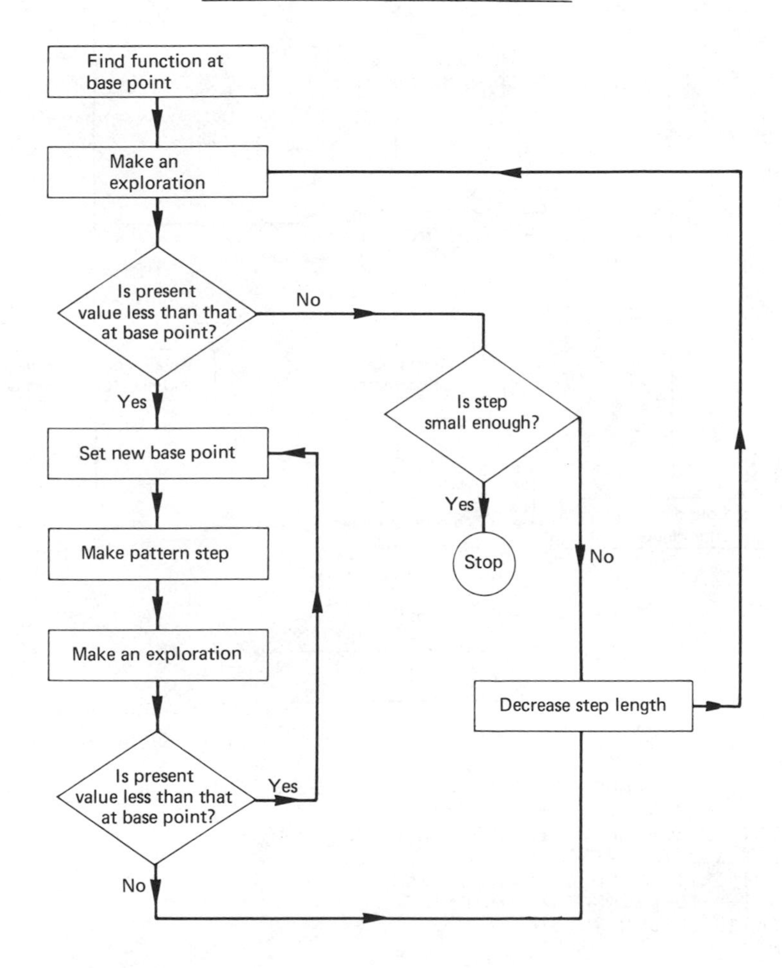

Flow Chart for an Exploration

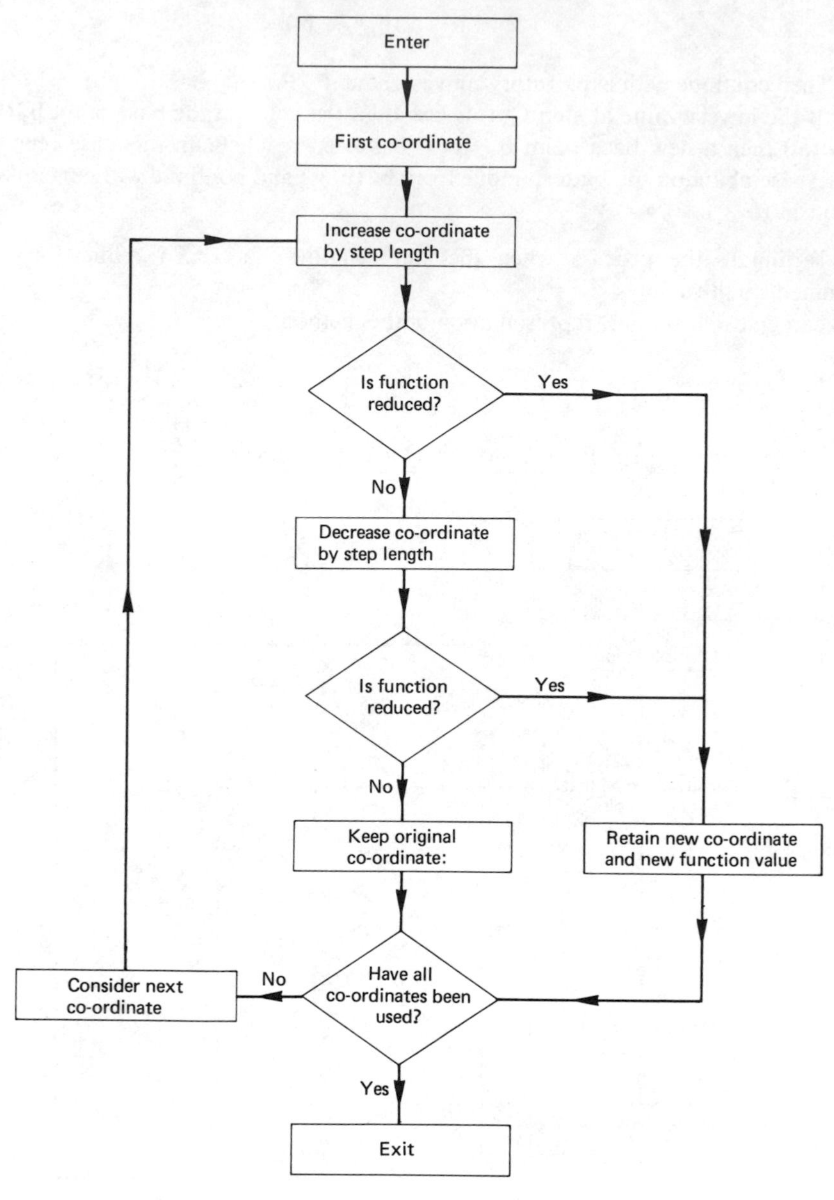


```
READY.

 10 PRINT"       HOOKE & JEEVES"
 20 REM Z=F(X1,X2,...,XN) AT 2000
 30 PRINT"NUMBER OF VARIABLES":INPUT N
 40 DIM X(N),B(N),Y(N),P(N)
 50 PRINT"INITIAL POINT X1,X2,..XN"
 60 FOR I=1 TO N:INPUT X(I):NEXT I
 70 PRINT"STEP LENGTH":INPUT H
 80 K=H
```

```
90 FOR I=1 TO N
100 Y(I)=X(I):P(I)=X(I):B(I)=X(I):NEXT I
110 GOSUB 2000:FI=Z
120 PRINT "INITIAL VALUE"Z
130 FOR I=1 TO N:PRINT X(I),:NEXT I:PRINT""
140 PS=0:BS=1
150 REM EXPLORE ABOUT BASE POINT
180 J=1:FB=FI
200 X(J)=Y(J)+K
210 GOSUB 2000
220 IF Z<FI THEN GOTO 280
230 X(J)=Y(J)-K
240 GOSUB 2000
250 IF Z<FI THEN GOTO 280
260 X(J)=Y(J)
270 GOTO 290
280 Y(J)=X(J)
290 GOSUB 2000
300 FI=Z
310 PRINT"EXPLORATION STEP"Z
320 FOR I=1 TO N:PRINT X(I),:NEXT I:PRINT""
330 IF J=N THEN GOTO 360
340 J=J+1
350 GOTO 200
360 IF FI<FB-1E-08 THEN GOTO 540
370 REM AFTER 360 MAKE A PATTERN MOVE IF FUNCTION HAS BEEN REDUCED
380 IF PS=1 AND BS=0 THEN GOTO 420
390 REM BUT IF EXPLORATION WAS ABOUT A PATTERN PT.
395 REM AND NO REDUCTION WAS MADE CHANGE BASE AT 420
400 REM OTHERWISE REDUCE STEP LENGTH AT 490
410 GOTO 490
420 FOR I=1 TO N:P(I)=B(I):Y(I)=B(I):X(I)=B(I):NEXT I
430 GOSUB 2000:BS=1:PS=0
440 FI=Z:FB=Z
450 PRINT"BASE CHANGE"Z
460 FOR I=1 TO N:PRINT X(I),:NEXT I:PRINT""
470 REM (FOLLOW ON FROM 395)AND EXPLORE ABOUT NEW BASE POINT
480 J=1:GOTO 200
490 K=K/10
500 PRINT"CONTRACT STEP LENGTH"
510 IF K< 1E-08 THEN GOTO 700
520 REM IF WE HAVE NOT FINISHED MAKE NEW
525 REM EXPLORATION ABOUT LATEST BASE POINT
530 J=1:GOTO 200
535 REM PATTERN MOVE
540 FOR I=1 TO N:P(I)=2*Y(I)-B(I)
550 B(I)=Y(I):X(I)=P(I):Y(I)=X(I)
560 NEXT I
570 GOSUB 2000:FB=FI:PS=1:BS=0:FI=Z
580 PRINT"PATTERN MOVE"Z
590 FOR I=1 TO N:PRINT X(I),:NEXT I:PRINT""
600 REM THEN EXPLORE ABOUT LATEST PATTERN POINT
610 J=1:GOTO 200
700 PRINT"        MINIMUM FOUND"
710 FOR I=1 TO N:PRINT"X"I"="P(I):NEXT I:PRINT""
750 PRINT"FUNCTION MINIMUM="FB
760 PRINT"NO. OF FUNCTION EVALUATIONS="FE
790 END
2000 Z=(X(1)-2)↑2+(X(2)-5)↑2+(X(3)+2)↑4
2010 FE=FE+1
2020 REM COUNTS FUNCTION EVALUATIONS
2030 RETURN
READY.
```

The program given implements the procedure. One or two points are worth noting. The first point always needs to be borne in mind. The computer only works to *finite* accuracy and errors can accumulate during the course of a complicated calculation, particularly in this case if the step length is an awkward size. (Normally we would avoid this but the program should be robust.) Thus at line 36Ø, where we are really asking if the base point has been changed, we avoid a reduction due to an accumulated error by inserting the 10^{-8}. We keep track of whether we are doing an exploration about a base point (BS = 1, PS = 0) or a pattern point (PS = 1, BS = 0) by means of these indicators. Experience shows that unless precautions of this type are taken, perfectly logical programs will fail.

As listed the minimum step length is 10^{-8} but this could be varied (line 51Ø). Intermediate output is given which allows the procedure to be monitored. To speed up the computation lines 12Ø, 13Ø, 31Ø, 32Ø, 45Ø, 46Ø, 5ØØ, 58Ø, 59Ø could be removed.

The subroutine at line 2ØØØ enables the function

$$f(x_1, x_2, x_3) = (x_1 - 2)^2 + (x_2 - 5)^2 + (x_3 + 2)^4$$

to be minimised. The minimum clearly is located at (2, 5, −2). Some of the output with (4, −2, 3) as the initial point and with initial step length as 1 is given. The progress of the explorations and pattern moves can be easily followed. Note the value 97·000 000 1 $(0^2 + 4^2 + 3^4 = 97)$ which illustrates the point made earlier. A count of the number of function evaluations needed is kept. This is often used as a means of comparing the efficiency of different search methods. The better the method, the fewer evaluations needed in general.

```
        HOOKE & JEEVES
NUMBER OF VARIABLES             3
INITIAL POINT X1,X2,..XN        4,-2,3
STEP LENGTH                     1
INITIAL VALUE 678
 4           -2                 3
EXPLORATION STEP 675
 3           -2                 3
EXPLORATION STEP 662
 3           -1                 3
EXPLORATION STEP 293
 3           -1                 2
PATTERN MOVE 1Ø6
 2            Ø                 1
EXPLORATION STEP 1Ø6
 2            Ø                 1
EXPLORATION STEP 97.ØØØØØØ1
 2            1                 1
EXPLORATION STEP 32
 2            1                 Ø
PATTERN MOVE 5
 1            3                -2
EXPLORATION STEP 4
 2            3                -2
EXPLORATION STEP 1
 2            4                -2
EXPLORATION STEP 1
 2            4                -2
PATTERN MOVE 2Ø
 2            7                -4
```

```
EXPLORATION STEP 20
 2          7              -4
EXPLORATION STEP 17
 2          6              -4
EXPLORATION STEP 2
 2          6              -3
BASE CHANGE 1
 2          4              -2
EXPLORATION STEP 1
 2          4              -2

.........................................

EXPLORATION STEP 0
 2          5              -2
EXPLORATION STEP 0
 2          5              -2
CONTRACT STEP LENGTH
      MINIMUM FOUND
X 1 = 2
X 2 = 5
X 3 =-2

FUNCTION MINIMUM= 0
NO. OF FUNCTION EVALUATIONS= 136
```

3.3 Nelder and Mead's Method

Nelder and Mead's method is an extension of the simplex method of Spendley, Hext and Himsworth. A set of $(n + 1)$ mutually equidistant points in n-dimensional space is known as a regular simplex. This figure underlies the Spendley, Hext and Himsworth method. Thus in two dimensions the simplex is an equilateral triangle and in three dimensions it is a regular tetrahedron. The idea of the method is to compare the values of the function at the $(n + 1)$ vertices of the simplex and move the simplex towards the optimum point during the iterative process. The original simplex method maintained a regular simplex at each stage. Nelder and Mead proposed several modifications to the method which allow the simplices to become non-regular. The result is a very robust direct search method which is extremely powerful provided that the number of variables does not exceed five or six.

The movement of the simplex in this method is achieved by the application of three basic operations *reflection*, *expansion* and *contraction*. The thinking underlying these operations will become clear as we consider the steps in the procedure.

(A) We start with $(n + 1)$ points $\mathbf{x}_1, \mathbf{x}_2, \ldots, \mathbf{x}_{n+1}$ and find

$$f_1 = f(\mathbf{x}_1), \quad f_2 = f(\mathbf{x}_2) \quad \ldots \quad f_{n+1} = f(\mathbf{x}_{n+1}).$$

(B) We find the highest function value f_h, the next highest function value f_g and the lowest function value f_l and the corresponding points $\mathbf{x}_h$, $\mathbf{x}_g$ and $\mathbf{x}_l$.

(C) Find the centroid of all the points except $\mathbf{x}_h$. Let this be $\mathbf{x}_0$ and evaluate $f(\mathbf{x}_0) = f_0$.

$$\mathbf{x}_0 = \frac{1}{n} \sum_{i \neq h} \mathbf{x}_i \tag{3.6}$$

(D) It would seem reasonable to try to move away from $\mathbf{x}_h$. We *reflect* $\mathbf{x}_h$ in $\mathbf{x}_0$ to find $\mathbf{x}_r$ and find $f(\mathbf{x}_r) = f_r$.

Reflection is illustrated in Fig. 3.2.

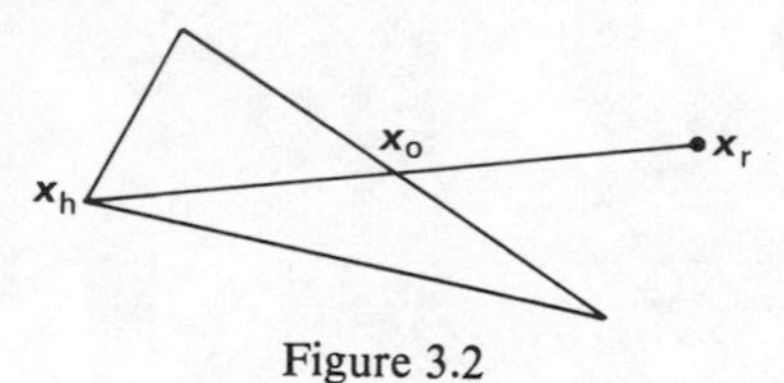

Figure 3.2

If $\alpha > 0$ is the *reflection* factor we find $\mathbf{x}_r$ such that

$$\mathbf{x}_r - \mathbf{x}_0 = \alpha(\mathbf{x}_0 - \mathbf{x}_h)$$

$$\text{i.e.} \quad \mathbf{x}_r = (1 + \alpha)\,\mathbf{x}_0 - \alpha\mathbf{x}_h. \tag{3.7}$$

$$\text{N.B.} \quad \alpha = |\mathbf{x}_r - \mathbf{x}_0| / |\mathbf{x}_0 - \mathbf{x}_h|.$$

(E) We now compare f_r with f_l.

(i) If $f_r < f_l$ we have obtained the lowest function value yet. The direction from $\mathbf{x}_0$ to $\mathbf{x}_r$ appears to be a good one to move along. We therefore make an *expansion* in this direction to find $\mathbf{x}_e$ and evaluate $f_e = f(\mathbf{x}_e)$. Figure 3.3 illustrates the operation of expanding the simplex. With an expansion factor γ (>1) we shall have

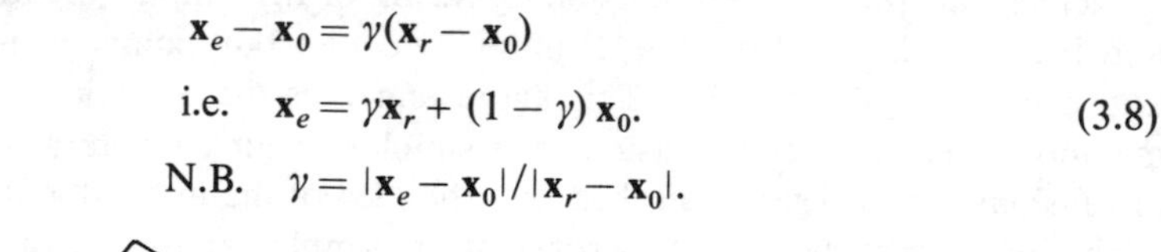

$$\mathbf{x}_e - \mathbf{x}_0 = \gamma(\mathbf{x}_r - \mathbf{x}_0)$$

$$\text{i.e.} \quad \mathbf{x}_e = \gamma\mathbf{x}_r + (1 - \gamma)\,\mathbf{x}_0. \tag{3.8}$$

$$\text{N.B.} \quad \gamma = |\mathbf{x}_e - \mathbf{x}_0| / |\mathbf{x}_r - \mathbf{x}_0|.$$

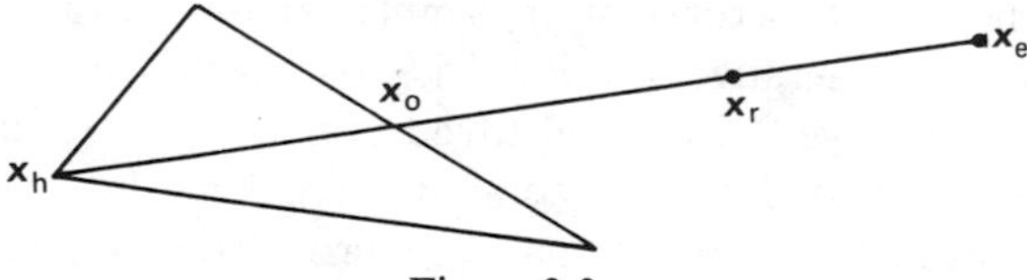

Figure 3.3

(a) if $f_e < f_l$ replace $\mathbf{x}_h$ by $\mathbf{x}_e$ and test the $(n + 1)$ points of the simplex for convergence to the minimum (see step (I)). If we have converged stop; if not return to step (B).

(b) If $f_e \nless f_l$ we abandon $\mathbf{x}_e$. We have evidently moved too far in the direction $\mathbf{x}_0$ to $\mathbf{x}_r$. Instead replace $\mathbf{x}_h$ by $\mathbf{x}_r$ which we know gave an improvement [step (E)(i)], test for convergence and if not return to step (B).

(ii) If $f_r > f_l$ but $f_r \ngtr f_g$, $\mathbf{x}_r$ is an improvement on the two worst points of the simplex and we replace $\mathbf{x}_h$ by $\mathbf{x}_r$, test for convergence and if not return to step (B); i.e. (i)(b) above.

(iii) If $f_r > f_l$ and $f_r > f_g$ proceed to step (F).

(F) We next compare f_r and f_h.

(i) If $f_r > f_h$ proceed directly to the *contraction* step (F)(ii).

If $f_r < f_h$ replace $\mathbf{x}_h$ by $\mathbf{x}_r$ and f_h by f_r. Remember $f_r > f_g$ from step (E)(iii) above.

Then proceed to step (F)(ii).
(ii) In this case $f_r > f_h$ so it would appear that we have moved too far in the direction $\mathbf{x}_h$ to $\mathbf{x}_0$. We try to rectify this by finding $\mathbf{x}_c$ (and then f_c) by a contraction step which is illustrated in Fig. 3.4.

If $f_r > f_h$ we proceed directly to the contraction and find $\mathbf{x}_c$ from

$$\mathbf{x}_c - \mathbf{x}_0 = \beta(\mathbf{x}_h - \mathbf{x}_0)$$

where β $(0 < \beta < 1)$ is the contraction coefficient. Thus

$$\mathbf{x}_c = \beta \mathbf{x}_h + (1 - \beta)\,\mathbf{x}_0 \tag{3.9}$$

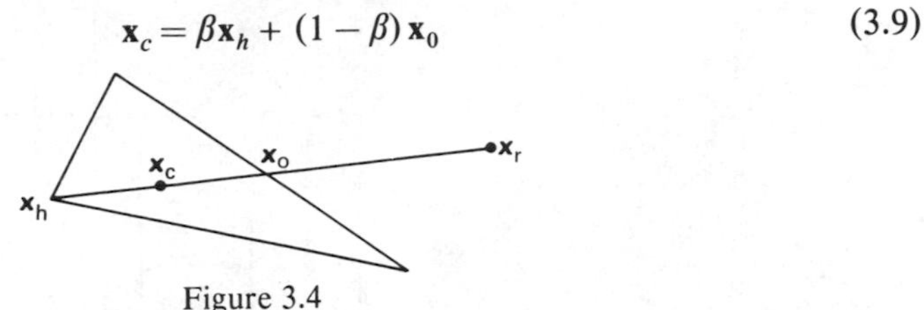

Figure 3.4

If however $f_r < f_h$ we first replace $\mathbf{x}_h$ by $\mathbf{x}_r$ and then contract. Thus we find $\mathbf{x}_c$ from

$$\mathbf{x}_c - \mathbf{x}_0 = \beta(\mathbf{x}_r - \mathbf{x}_0)$$

$$\text{i.e.} \quad \mathbf{x}_c = \beta \mathbf{x}_r + (1 - \beta)\,\mathbf{x}_0. \tag{3.10}$$

See Fig. 3.5.

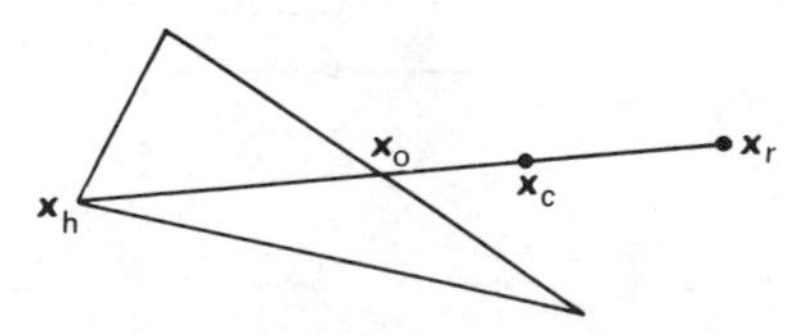

Figure 3.5

(G) We now compare f_c and f_h.
(i) If $f_c < f_h$ we replace $\mathbf{x}_h$ by $\mathbf{x}_c$, check for convergence and if not return to step (B).
(ii) If $f_c > f_h$ it would appear that all our efforts to find a value $< f_h$ have failed so we move to step (H).

(H) At this step we reduce the size of the simplex by halving the distance of each point of the simplex from $\mathbf{x}_l$ the point generating the lowest function value.

Thus $\mathbf{x}_i$ is replaced by $\mathbf{x}_l + \frac{1}{2}(\mathbf{x}_i - \mathbf{x}_l)$
i.e. replace $\mathbf{x}_i$ by

$$\tfrac{1}{2}(\mathbf{x}_i + \mathbf{x}_l). \tag{3.11}$$

We then calculate f_i for $i = 1, 2, \ldots, (n + 1)$, test for convergence and if not return to step (B).

(I) The test of convergence is based on the standard deviation of the $(n + 1)$ function values being less than some pre-determined small value ε. Thus we calculate

$$\sigma^2 = \sum_{i=1}^{n+1} (f_i - \bar{f})^2/(n + 1) \tag{3.12}$$

where $\bar{f} = \sum f_i/n + 1$.

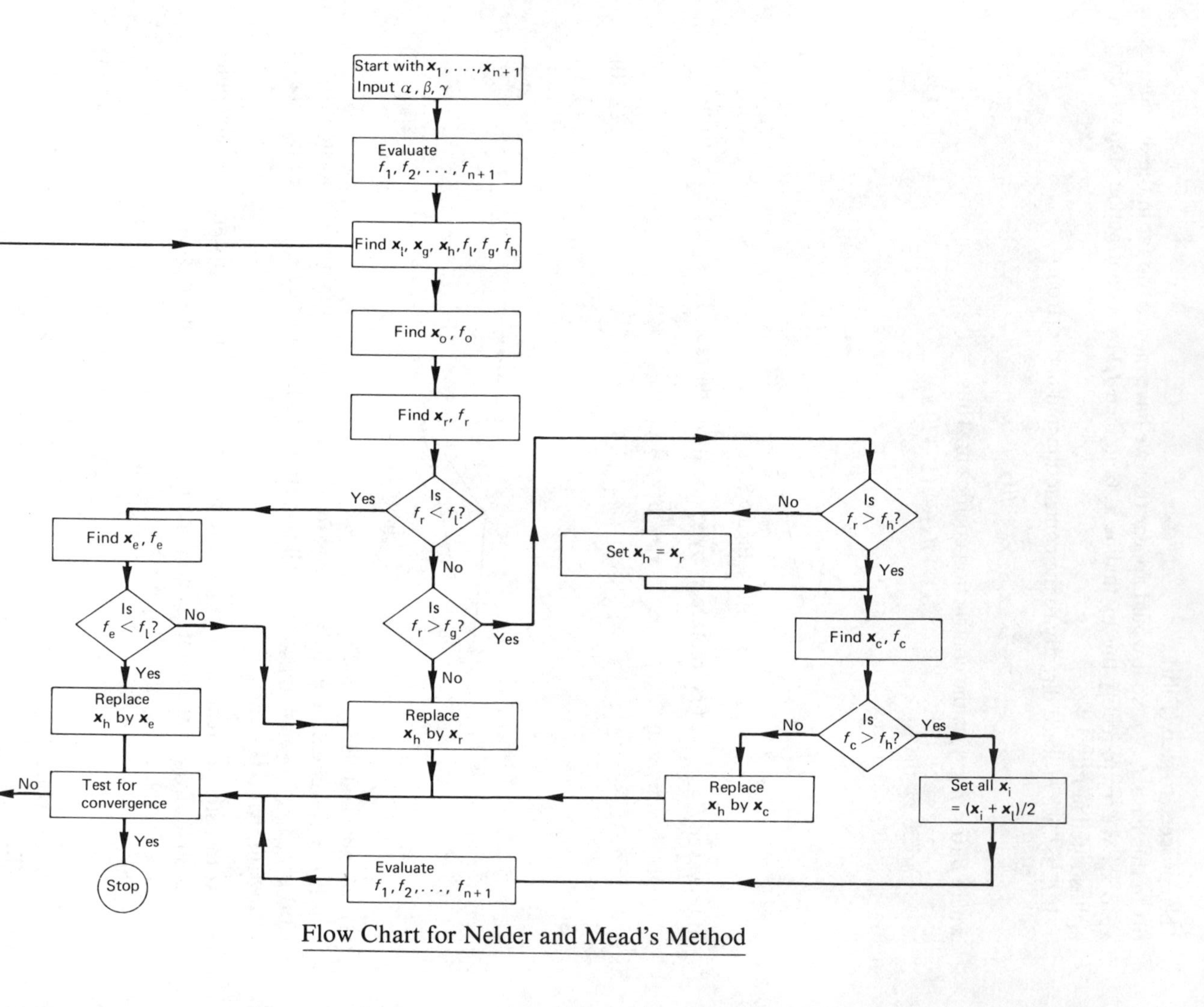

Flow Chart for Nelder and Mead's Method

If $\sigma < \varepsilon$ all function values are very close together, and so hopefully are the points, near the minimum $\mathbf{x}_l$. This convergence criterion is thus reasonable although Box, Davies and Swann (reference 1) suggest what they regard as a 'safer' test.

We give a flow chart for the steps in the procedure on the opposite page.

There remain some important details to clarify. The first concerns the values of α, β, γ which occur as the reflection, contraction and expansion coefficients respectively. Nelder and Mead recommend $\alpha = 1$, $\beta = 0{\cdot}5$, $\gamma = 2$. This recommendation is based on trials with many different combinations. It appears to allow the method to work efficiently in many different situations.

The choice of the initial simplex is at our discretion. The program given takes an initial point $\mathbf{x}_1$ and then forms

$$\begin{aligned} \mathbf{x}_2 &= \mathbf{x}_1 + k\mathbf{e}_1 \\ \mathbf{x}_3 &= \mathbf{x}_1 + k\mathbf{e}_2 \\ \mathbf{x}_{n+1} &= \mathbf{x}_1 + k\mathbf{e}_n \end{aligned} \tag{3.13}$$

where k is an (arbitrary) step length of our choice and $\mathbf{e}_j$ is a unit vector in the direction of the jth co-ordinate.

The notation used in the program follows that of the text in general, except that upper case symbols are used, FE $\equiv f_e$; XC $\equiv \mathbf{x}_c$ etc. The points of the simplex are donated by S. S(I, J) is the Jth component of the Ith point.

$$\text{S(I, J)} \equiv x_{ij} \tag{3.14}$$

The program follows the flow chart, and read in conjunction with the 'print' statements for input, and the 'rem' statements should be easy to follow. As listed, the subroutine at line 5ØØØ is appropriate to minimise Powell's function (equation 3.2).

Note that the test for convergence (lines 2Ø6Ø–218Ø) uses the well known identity

$$\sum_{i=1}^{n+1} (f_i - \bar{f})^2 = \sum_{i=1}^{n+1} f_i^2 - (n+1)\,\bar{f}^2 \tag{3.15}$$

to calculate the first quantity.

The program listing follows.

```
READY.

 2Ø PRINT"SIMPLEX METHOD OF NELDER & MEAD"
 4Ø PRINT""
 6Ø PRINT"Z=F(X1,X2,...,XN) AT 5ØØØ"
 8Ø PRINT""
 1ØØ PRINT"ENTER NO. OF VARIABLES"
 12Ø INPUT N
 14Ø PRINT"INITIAL ESTIMATE"
 16Ø DIM S(N+1,N)
 18Ø FOR J=1 TO N
 2ØØ INPUT S(1,J)
 22Ø NEXT J
 24Ø PRINT"ENTER STEP LENGTH"
 26Ø INPUT K
 27Ø REM SET UP FIRST SIMPLEX AROUND INITIAL POINT
 28Ø FOR I=2 TO N+1
 3ØØ FOR J=1 TO N
 32Ø IF J=I-1 THEN S(I,J)=S(1,J)+K:GOTO 36Ø
 34Ø S(I,J)=S(1,J)
```

```
360 NEXT J
380 NEXT I
400 PRINT"ENTER ALPHA,BETA,GAMMA"
420 INPUT AL,BE,GA
440 DIM X(N),XH(N),XG(N),XL(N),XO(N)
460 DIM XR(N),XC(N),XE(N),F(N+1)
470 REM FIND FUNCTION VALUES
480 FOR I=1 TO N+1
500 FOR J=1 TO N
520 X(J)=S(I,J)
540 NEXT J
560 GOSUB 5000
580 F(I)=Z
600 NEXT I
610 REM FIND GREATEST AND LOWEST FUNCTION
615 REM VALUES AND CORRESPONDING POINTS
620 FH=-1E20:FL=1E20
640 FOR I=1 TO N+1
660 IF F(I)>FH THEN FH=F(I):H=I
680 IF F(I)<FL THEN FL=F(I):L=I
700 NEXT I
710 REM FIND SECOND GREATEST VALUE AND POINT.
720 FG=-1E20
740 FOR I=1 TO N+1
760 IF I=H THEN GOTO 800
780 IF F(I)>FG THEN FG=F(I):G=I
800 NEXT I
820 FOR J=1 TO N
840 XO(J)=0
860 FOR I=1 TO N+1
880 IF I=H THEN GOTO 910
900 XO(J)=XO(J)+S(I,J)
910 NEXT I
920 REM IDENTIFY X0,XH,XG,XL
940 XO(J)=XO(J)/N
960 XH(J)=S(H,J)
980 XG(J)=S(G,J)
1000 XL(J)=S(L,J)
1020 NEXT J
1040 FOR J=1 TO N
1060 X(J)=XO(J)
1080 NEXT J
1100 GOSUB 5000
1120 FO=Z:PRINT"CENTROID AT 1120"
1130 REM REFLECTION FOLLOWS
1140 FOR J=1 TO N
1160 XR(J)=XO(J)+AL*(XO(J)-XH(J))
1180 X(J)=XR(J)
1200 NEXT J
1220 GOSUB 5000:FR=Z:PRINT"REFLECTION AT 1220";Z
1230 REM IF FR<FL EXPANSION
1240 IF FR<FL THEN GOTO 1300
1250 REM IF FR>FL AND FR>FG TEST FR AND FH
1255 REM OTHERWISE REPLACE XH BY XR
1260 IF FR>FG THEN GOTO 1600
1280 GOTO 1520
1290 REM EXPANSION FOLLOWS
1300 FOR J=1 TO N
1320 XE(J)=GA*XR(J)+(1-GA)*XO(J)
1340 X(J)=XE(J)
1360 NEXT J
1380 GOSUB 5000:FE=Z
1400 IF FE<FL THEN GOTO 1440
1420 GOTO 1520
```

```
1440 FOR J=1 TO N
1460 S(H.J)=XE(J)
1480 NEXT J:F(H)=FE:PRINT"EXPANSION AT 1480";Z
1490 REM TEST FOR CONVERGENCE IS AT 2060
1500 GOTO 2060
1520 FOR J=1 TO N
1540 S(H,J)=XR(J)
1560 NEXT J:F(H)=FR:PRINT"REFLECTION AT 1560"
1580 GOTO 2060
1600 IF FR>FH THEN GOTO 1700
1620 FOR J=1 TO N
1640 XH(J)=XR(J)
1660 NEXT J
1680 F(H)=FR
1690 REM CONTRACTION FOLLOWS
1700 FOR J=1 TO N
1720 XC(J)=BE*XH(J)+(1-BE)*XO(J)
1740 X(J)=XC(J)
1760 NEXT J
1780 GOSUB 5000:FC=Z
1800 IF FC>FH THEN GOTO 1920
1820 FOR J=1 TO N
1840 S(H,J)=XC(J)
1860 NEXT J
1880 F(H)=FC:PRINT"CONTRACTION AT 1880";Z
1900 GOTO 2060
1910 REM SIMPLEX REDUCTION FOLLOWS
1920 FOR I=1 TO N+1
1940 FOR J=1 TO N
1960 S(I,J)=(S(I,J)+XL(J))/2
1980 X(J)=S(I,J)
2000 NEXT J
2020 GOSUB 5000:F(I)=Z
2040 NEXT I:PRINT"REDUCTION AT 2040"
2050 REM TEST FOR CONVERGENCE FOLLOWS
2060 S1=0:S2=0
2080 FOR I=1 TO N+1
2100 S1+F(I)
2120 S2=S2+F(I)*F(I)
2140 NEXT I
2160 SIG=S2-S1*S1/N+1):SIG = SIG/(N+1)
2180 IF SIG <1E-10 THEN GOTO 2220
2200 GOTO 620
2220 PRINT"MINIMUM OBTAINED"
2240 FOR J=1 TO N
2260 PRINT"X"J"="XL(J)
2280 NEXT J:PRINT""
2300 PRINT"FUNCTION MINIMUM="F(L)
2320 PRINT"NO.OF F EVALS="TEV
2340 END
5000 Z=(X(1)+10*X(2))↑2+5*(X(3)-X(4))↑2
5020 Z=Z+(X(2)-2*X(3))↑4
5040 Z=Z+10*(X(1)-X(4))↑4
5060 TEV=TEV+1
5100 RETURN
READY.
```

Example 1

Use Nelder and Mead's method to minimise Rosenbrock's function

$$f(x_1, x_2) = 100(x_2 - x_1^2)^2 + (1 - x_1)^2.$$

Use the point (1·5, 2) as the initial estimate, take k as 0·5, and use $\alpha = 1$, $\beta = 0{\cdot}5$ and $\gamma = 2$.

With the subroutine at line 5ØØØ modified correctly the start and finish of the output follows. As given the progress of the procedure can be followed reasonably well. Of course it is possible to suppress the printout at lines 112Ø, 122Ø, 148Ø, 156Ø, 2Ø4Ø and this will speed up the operations.

The true minimum has value 0 at (1, 1).

```
SIMPLEX METHOD OF NELDER & MEAD

Z=F(X1,X2,...,XN) AT 5ØØØ

ENTER NO. OF VARIABLES    2
INITIAL ESTIMATE          1.5,2
ENTER STEP LENGTH         Ø.5
ENTER ALPHA,BETA,GAMMA    1,Ø.5,2
CENTROID AT 112Ø
REFLECTION AT 122Ø 225
CONTRACTION AT 188Ø 66.078125
CENTROID AT 112Ø
REFLECTION AT 122Ø 88.453125
CONTRACTION AT 188Ø 17.9384766
CENTROID AT 112Ø
REFLECTION AT 122Ø 2Ø.9228516
CONTRACTION AT 188Ø 4.8Ø718994
CENTROID AT 112Ø
REFLECTION AT 122Ø 51.2915649
CONTRACTION AT 188Ø .24111ØØ87
CENTROID AT 112Ø
REFLECTION AT 122Ø .381975412
REFLECTION AT 156Ø
CENTROID AT 112Ø
REFLECTION AT 122Ø 7.32736588
CONTRACTION AT 188Ø 1.Ø9445943

. . . . . . . . . . . . . . . . . . . . . . . . .

CENTROID AT 112Ø
REFLECTION AT 122Ø 6.87355313E-Ø5
REFLECTION AT 156Ø
CENTROID AT 112Ø
REFLECTION AT 122Ø 1.43423235E-Ø4
CONTRACTION AT 188Ø 2.77611111E-Ø5
CENTROID AT 112Ø
REFLECTION AT 122Ø 3.541Ø1169E-Ø5
CONTRACTION AT 188Ø 8.7954Ø528E-Ø6
CENTROID AT 112Ø
REFLECTION AT 122Ø 2.163Ø8611E-Ø5
CONTRACTION AT 188Ø 5.54464437E-Ø6
MINIMUM OBTAINED
X 1 = 1.ØØØ63318
X 2 = 1.ØØ135699

FUNCTION MINIMUM= 1.21515866E-Ø6
NO.OF F EVALS= 1Ø8
```

3.4 References

1 M. J. Box, D. Davies and W. H. Swann, *Non-linear Optimisation Techniques*, ICI Ltd., Monograph No. 5, Oliver and Boyd, 1969.

2 R. Hooke and T. A. Jeeves, 'Direct search solution of numerical and statistical problems', *J. Assn. Comp. Mach.*, **8**, 212–229, 1961.

3 J. A. Nelder and R. Mead, 'A simplex method for function minimisation', *The Comp. Journal*, **7**, 308–313, 1965.
4 M. J. D. Powell, 'An iterative method for finding stationary values of a function of several variables', *The Comp. Journal*, **5**, 147–151, 1962.
5 H. H. Rosenbrock, 'An automatic method for finding the greatest or least value of a function', *The Comp. Journal*, **3**, 175–184, 1960.
6 W. Spendley, G. R. Hext and F. R. Himsworth, 'Sequential applications of simplex designs in optimisation and evolutionary operation', *Technometrics*, **4**, 441–461, 1962.

Exercises 3

1 Try to write a BASIC program to implement the alternating variable search procedure. You can use any of the one-dimensional searches of Chapter 2 as a subroutine for this procedure.

2 Use the program you have written in question 1 to find the minimum of (i) $(x_1 - 1)^2 + (x_2 - 2)^2 + (x_3 - 3)^2$ (ii) Rosenbrock's function $100(x_2 - x_1^2)^2 + (1 - x_1)^2$.

3 Use the Hooke and Jeeves program to minimise the functions of question 2. Compare the number of function evaluations needed with the number needed for the alternating variable procedure.

4 Repeat questions 2 and 3 but with a variety of initial points.

5 Modify the Hooke and Jeeves method, changing the factor which reduces the step length. Instead of 10 use (a) 2 (b) 4 (c) 8 (d) 100. Repeat the examples given in questions 2 and 3 (and any others) and compare the number of function evaluations needed to obtain the final result.

6 Use the Nelder and Mead program to minimise (i) Rosenbrock's function (ii) Powell's function (iii) the two dimensional exponential function. [Equations 3.1, 3.2, 3.3.] Use different starting values and compare the number of function evaluations. Particularly awkward starting points are $(-1{\cdot}2, 1)$ for (i) and $(3, -1, 0, 1)$ for (ii).

7 Consult the reference by Box, Davies and Swann. Try to incorporate their convergence test in the Nelder and Mead program and test the result on the functions of question 6.

8 Modify the Nelder and Mead program by using different values for α, β and γ. Test the results. Consult the paper by Nelder and Mead and read their comments on this point.

9 Consult the reference by Spendley, Hext and Himsworth. Write a BASIC program to implement their method and test it. How does it compare with Nelder and Mead in terms of the number of function evaluations required?

10 Minimise the function

$$f(x_1, x_2) = x_1^4 + x_2^4 + 2x_1^2 x_2^2 - 4x_1 + 3.$$

11 Minimise the function

$$\phi(x_1, x_2) = (x_1^2 + x_2 - 11)^2 + (x_1 + x_2^2 - 7)^2.$$

12 Solve the equations

$$x_1^2 + x_2 = 11$$

$$x_1 + x_2^2 = 7.$$

Can you see how you can use question 11 to help you?

13 Solve the equations

$$x + y + z = 6$$

$$x^2 + y^2 + z^2 = 14$$

$$x^3 + y^3 + z^3 = 36.$$

14 The variables F and C should follow a relationship of the form $F = a + bC$ but there is error in the measured value of F.

Estimate a and b given the data below

F	51	68	84	103	121	141
C	10	20	30	40	50	60

Use the principle of least squares and choose a and b to minimise

$$S = \sum_{i=1}^{6} (F_i - a - bC_i)^2.$$

This is a simple linear regression problem. This topic is considered in many elementary statistics books and formulae for a and b exist which are easy to calculate. Check your answer using these results.

15 It is known that the variables Q and h are related (subject to measured error in Q) by $Q = ah^n$ where a and n are constants.

Given the data below show that this appears to be reasonable and estimate a and n.

h	4	6	8	10	12
Q	650	1740	3640	6360	9790

N.B. If $Q = ah^n$, $\ln(Q) = \ln(a) + n\ln(h)$. Thus we can reduce the problem to one of linear regression with transformed variables $\ln(Q)$ and $\ln(h)$. Try it with and without the transformation from the point of view of the principle of least squares;

i.e. minimise (i) $S_1 = \sum [\ln(Q_i) - \ln(a) - n\ln(h_i)]^2$

(ii) $S_2 = \sum (Q_i - ah_i^n)^2$

by choice of a and n. Are the answers the same?

4
Gradient Methods

4.1 The Method of Steepest Descent

In this chapter we consider search methods which use the gradient of the function as well as the function values. The alternating variable search which was briefly mentioned in Section 3.1 searched from a given point in a direction parallel to one of the axes for the minimum in that direction. It then searched in a direction parallel to one of the other axes etc. The directions are of course fixed. It seems reasonable to try to modify this method so that at each step the search for the minimum is carried out along the 'best' direction. What is best is not clear but the direction opposite to that of the gradient has a certain intuitive appeal. The direction of the gradient is the direction of steepest ascent. The opposite direction is thus the direction of steepest descent.

This property can be proved as follows. Suppose from a point $\mathbf{x}$ we move to a neighbouring point $\mathbf{x} + h\mathbf{d}$ where $\mathbf{d}$ is some direction and h is some step length. Thus we move from $(x_1, x_2, \ldots, x_n)$ to $(x_1 + \delta x_1, x_2 + \delta x_2, \ldots, x_n + \delta x_n)$ where

$$\delta x_i = hd_i \tag{4.1}$$

and d_i are the direction cosines of $\mathbf{d}$ so that

$$\sum_{i=1}^{n} d_i^2 = 1. \tag{4.2}$$

The change in the function value is given by

$$\begin{aligned} \mathrm{d}f &= f(x_1 + \delta x_1, x_2 + \delta x_2, \ldots, x_n + \delta x_n) - f(x_1, x_2, \ldots, x_n) \\ &= \frac{\partial f}{\partial x_1}\,\delta x_1 + \frac{\partial f}{\partial x_2}\,\delta x_2 + \cdots + \frac{\partial f}{\partial x_n}\,\delta x_n \end{aligned} \tag{4.3}$$

to first order in the δx_i, where the partial derivatives are evaluated at $\mathbf{x}$ (refer to equation 1.4). How should we choose the d_i subject to equation 4.2 so that we obtain the largest possible value for $\mathrm{d}f$?

We have here a constrained maximisation problem, and to solve it, we anticipate the results of the next chapter. Thus we use the method of Lagrange multipliers to define

$$\phi(d_1, d_2, \ldots, d_n) = \mathrm{d}f + \lambda(\textstyle\sum d_i^2 - 1)$$

The maximum of $\mathrm{d}f$ subject to the constraint (equation 4.2) arises when $\phi(d_1, d_2, \ldots, d_n)$ is maximised.

$$\phi(d_1, d_2, \ldots, d_n) = h\left(\frac{\partial f}{\partial x_1}\,d_1 + \frac{\partial f}{\partial x_2}\,d_2 + \cdots + \frac{\partial f}{\partial x_n}\,d_n\right) + \lambda(d_1^2 + d_2^2 + \cdots + d_n^2 - 1)$$

$$\frac{\partial \phi}{\partial d_j} = h\,\frac{\partial f}{\partial x_j} + 2\lambda d_j \quad (j = 1, 2, \ldots, n). \tag{4.4}$$

When

$$\frac{\partial \phi}{\partial d_j} = 0, \quad d_j = -\frac{h}{2\lambda}\frac{\partial f}{\partial x_j}. \tag{4.5}$$

$$\therefore \quad \frac{d_1}{\dfrac{\partial f}{\partial x_1}} = \frac{d_2}{\dfrac{\partial f}{\partial x_2}} = \cdots = \frac{d_n}{\dfrac{\partial f}{\partial x_n}}. \tag{4.6}$$

Thus $d_i \propto \partial f / \partial x_i$ and the direction $\mathbf{d}$ is parallel to $\nabla f(\mathbf{x})$ at $\mathbf{x}$.

Thus the greatest *local* increase in the function for a given *small* step h occurs when $\mathbf{d}$ is in the direction of $\nabla f(\mathbf{x})$ or $\mathbf{g}(\mathbf{x})$. So the direction of steepest descent is in the direction

$$-\nabla f(\mathbf{x}) \quad \text{or} \quad -\mathbf{g}(\mathbf{x}). \tag{4.7}$$

More simply we can write equation 4.3 as

$$\mathrm{d}f = |\nabla f(\mathbf{x})| \, |\mathrm{d}\mathbf{x}| \cos \theta$$

where θ is the angle between $\nabla f(\mathbf{x})$ and $\mathrm{d}\mathbf{x}$. For a given magnitude of $\mathrm{d}\mathbf{x}$ we minimise $\mathrm{d}f$ by choosing θ to be 180° so that $\mathrm{d}\mathbf{x}$ is in the direction $-\nabla f(\mathbf{x})$.

N.B. The gradient direction is orthogonal to the contours of the function at any point, for on a contour the function value does not change. Thus if $(d_1, d_2, \ldots, d_n)$ is a *small* step along the contour

$$f(x_1 + d_1, x_2 + d_2, \ldots, x_n + d_n) = f(x_1, x_2, \ldots, x_n)$$

$$\therefore \quad \mathrm{d}f = \sum_{j=1}^{n} \frac{\partial f}{\partial x_j} d_j = [\nabla f(\mathbf{x})]^{\mathrm{T}} \mathbf{d} = 0. \tag{4.8}$$

See Fig. 4.1.

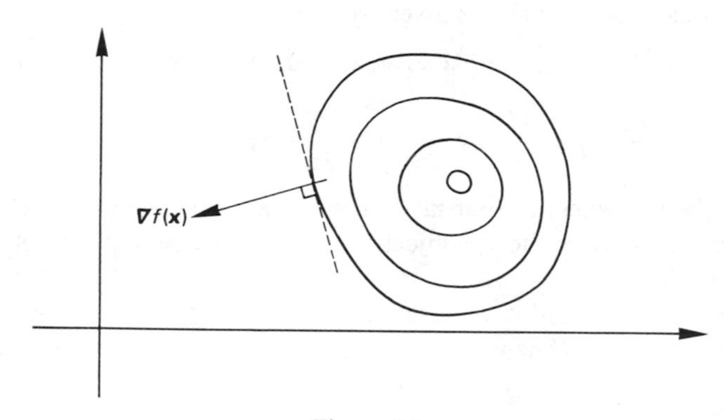

Figure 4.1

The method of steepest descent seeks to exploit this property of the gradient direction. Thus if we are at the point $\mathbf{x}_i$ at any stage in the process we search for the function minimum along the direction $-\nabla f(\mathbf{x}_i)$. The method is an iterative process. At stage i we have an approximation $\mathbf{x}_i$ for the minimum point. Our next approximation is

$$\mathbf{x}_{i+1} = \mathbf{x}_i - \lambda_i \nabla f(\mathbf{x}_i) \tag{4.9}$$

where λ_i is the value of λ that minimises

$$\phi(\lambda) = f[\mathbf{x}_i - \lambda\nabla f(\mathbf{x}_i)] \tag{4.10}$$

λ_i can be found by using one of the univariate searches of Chapter 2. A flow chart for the method follows.

Flow Chart for Steepest Descent

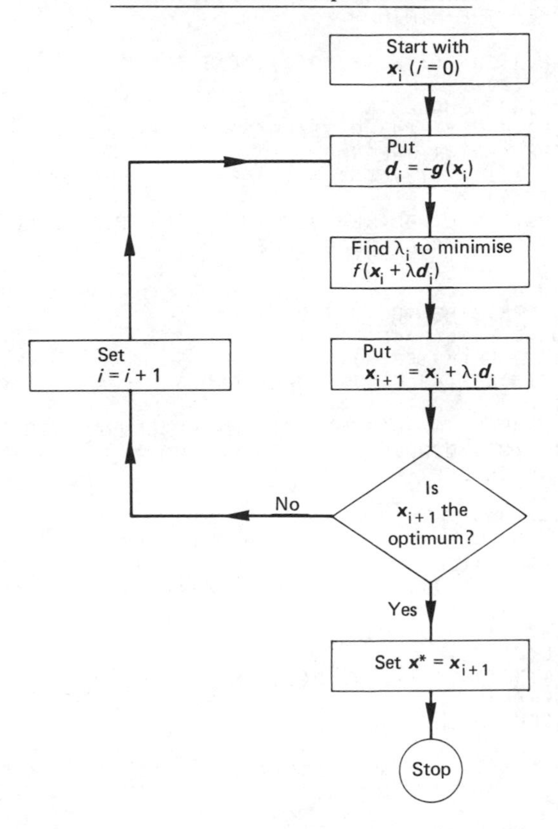


```
READY.

 2Ø PRINT"        STEEPEST DESCENT"
 4Ø PRINT"Z=F(X1,X2...XN) AT 2ØØØ"
 6Ø PRINT"PARTIAL DERIVATIVES G(1),G(2)...G(N) AT 3ØØØ-"
 8Ø PRINT" LINEAR SEARCHES BY QUADRATIC INTERPOLATION"
 1ØØ PRINT"NO. OF VARIABLES":INPUT N
 12Ø DIM X(N),Y(N),G(N),D(N),L(4),FF(4)
 14Ø REM L(4)&FF(4) FOR QUAD.INT.
 16Ø PRINT"INITIAL POINT"
 18Ø FOR I=1 TO N:INPUT X(I):NEXT I
 2ØØ PRINT"INITIAL STEP":INPUT L
 25Ø PRINT"        CURRENT VALUES"
 26Ø REM HEADING FOR INTERMEDIATE OUTPUT
 3ØØ FOR I=1 TO N:Y(I)=X(I):NEXT I
 32Ø GOSUB 2ØØØ:GOSUB 3ØØØ:IF GØ<Ø.ØØØØØ1 THEN GOTO 12ØØ
 34Ø FOR I=1 TO N:D(I)=-G(I)/GØ:NEXT I
 36Ø REM SET DIRECTION OF STEEPEST DESCENT FROM Y(I)
 37Ø REM [=X(I) AT FIRST]
 38Ø L(1)=Ø:FF(1)=Z:ZZ=Z
```

```
 400 L(3)=L
 410 FOR I=1 TO N:X(I)=Y(I)+L(3)*D(I):NEXT I
 430 GOSUB 2000:FF(3)=Z
 440 GOSUB 3000
 450 G2=0
 460 FOR I=1 TO N:G2=G2+G(I)*D(I):NEXT I
 470 IF FF(3)>=FF(1) OR G2>=0 THEN GOTO 500
 480 L=2*L:GOTO 400
 500 REM IF WE OBEY 480 WE DOUBLE STEP LENGTH
 510 REM TO BRACKET THE MINIMUM
 520 L(2)=L/2
 540 FOR I=1 TO N:X(I)=Y(I)+L(2)*D(I):NEXT I
 560 GOSUB 2000:FF(2)=Z
 580 REM NOW DO FIRST QUAD. INT.
 600 L(4)=L*(FF(2)-0.75*FF(1)-0.25*FF(3))/(2*FF(2)-FF(1)-FF(3))
 620 IF L(4)<0 THEN PRINT "ALARM"
 640 FOR I=1 TO N:X(I)=Y(I)+L(4)*D(I):NEXT I
 660 GOSUB 2000:FF(4)=Z
 680 REM WE NOW HAVE 4 LAMBDA VALUES AND 4 FUNCTION VALUES
 690 REM WE PUT THEM IN ASCENDING ORDER
 700 FOR J=1 TO 3
 710 FOR K=J+1 TO 4
 720 IF FF(J)<= FF(K) THEN GOTO 760
 730 LL=L(J):L(J)=L(K):L(K)=LL
 740 F0=FF(J):FF(J)=FF(K):FF(K)=F0
 750 REM SWAPS FF(J)&FF(K) IF IN WRONG ORDER
 760 NEXT K:NEXT J
 790 REM FINISH SEARCH IN THIS DIRECTION IF ACCURACY IS OK AT 800
 800 IF ABS(L(1)-L(2))<0.00005 THEN GOTO 1000
 810 REM RETAIN THREE BEST POINTS
 820 S1=SGN(L(2)-L(1)):S2=SGN(L(3)-L(1))
 830 S3=SGN(L(4)-L(1))
 840 IF S1=S2 AND S1=-S4 THEN L(3)=L(4):FF(3)=FF(4)
 850 REM SECOND AND LATER INTERPOLATIONS
 860 DN=(L(2)-L(3))*FF(1)+(L(3)-L(1))*FF(2)+(L(1)-L(2))*FF(3)
 870 F=(FF(1)-FF(2))/(2*DN)
 880 F=F*(L(2)-L(3))*(L(3)-L(1))
 890 L(4)=(L(1)+L(2))/2+F
 900 FOR I=1 TO N:X(I)=Y(I)+L(4)*D(I):NEXT I
 910 GOSUB 2000:FF(4)=Z
 920 REM REPEAT SECOND INTERPOLATION
 930 GOTO 700
 1000 FOR I=1 TO N:X(I)=Y(I)+L(1)*D(I):Y(I)=X(I):PRINT"X"I"="X(I)
 1005 NEXT I
 1010 PRINT""
 1020 GOSUB 2000:GOSUB 3000
 1040 PRINT"F="Z:PRINT""
 1080 L=L/2
 1100 IF G0>0.00001 THEN GOTO 340
 1150 REM THIS WILL START ANOTHER SEARCH FROM CURRENT POSITION
 1200 PRINT"":PRINT
 1210 PRINT"          FINAL SOLUTION"
 1220 FOR I=1 TO N:PRINT"X"I"="X(I):NEXT I
 1240 PRINT"MINIMUM OF F(X1,X2...XN)="Z
 1300 END
 2000 Z=(X(1)-1)↑2+(X(2)-3)↑2+4*(X(3)+5)↑2
 2090 FE=FE+1
 2100 RETURN
 3000 G0=0
 3100 G(1)=2*(X(1)-1)
 3200 G(2)=2*(X(2)-3)
 3300 G(3)=8*(X(3)+5)
 3800 FOR I=1 TO N:G0=G0+G(I)*G(I):NEXT I
 3810 G0=SQR(G0)
 4000 RETURN
READY.
```

A program to carry out the procedure is given. It uses the notation of the flow chart using capital letters and L for λ. The $\mathbf{d}_i$ at line 34Ø is set equal to a unit vector in the direction of steepest descent.

We use quadratic interpolation to find the minimum of

$$\phi(\lambda) = f(\mathbf{x}_i + \lambda \mathbf{d}_i) \tag{4.11}$$

when we search from $\mathbf{x}_i$ in the direction $\mathbf{d}_i$.

At $\mathbf{x}_i$, $\lambda = 0$ and we choose our step length λ so that we span the minimum of $\phi(\lambda)$. Note that

$$\frac{d\phi}{d\lambda} = \mathbf{g}(\mathbf{x}_i + \lambda \mathbf{d}_i)^T \mathbf{d}_i. \tag{4.12}$$

See also equation 2.16. This is calculated as G2 at line 46Ø. Thus at line 47Ø we are sure to have spanned the minimum if either $\phi(\lambda) \geqslant \phi(0)$ or $d\phi(\lambda)/d\lambda$ (=G2) $\geqslant 0$.

N.B. $d\phi(0)/d\lambda = -\mathbf{g}(\mathbf{x}_i)^T \mathbf{g}(\mathbf{x}_i) < 0$. See Fig. 4.2(i) and (ii).

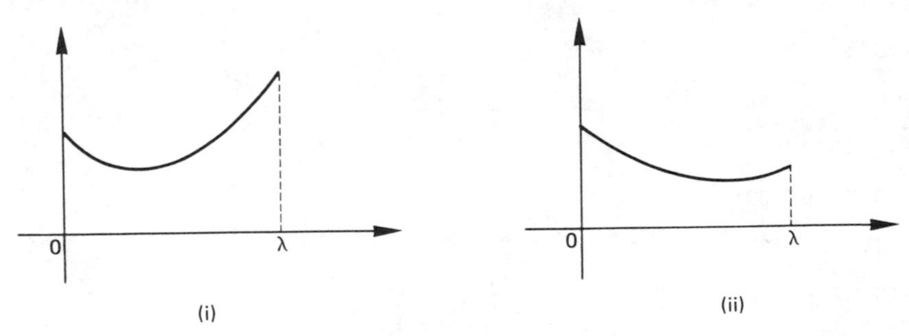

Figure 4.2

If we have not bracketed a minimum we double λ, repeatedly if necessary, until we do.

Having ascertained that $(0, \lambda)$ includes the minimum we choose our third point as $\lambda/2$. We find the minimum point of the fitted quadratic using the special form of equation 2.12 in question 8 of Exercises 2 with $t = \lambda/2$. This appears at line 6ØØ.

The quadratic interpolation now follows the program given in Section 2.4 except that the line numbers are increased by 3ØØ. The accuracy specified at 8ØØ could of course be changed.

At line 1ØØØ we reset the point $\mathbf{x}_i \to \mathbf{x}_{i+1}$ and if $|\mathbf{g}(\mathbf{x}_{i+1})|$ is small enough we terminate (11ØØ). The step length is reduced at line 1Ø8Ø. As the searches proceed we hope to converge on the optimum so it seems reasonable that the step length should get smaller for an efficient procedure. However the division by 2 is arbitrary.

Example 1

Use the program given to find the minimum of

$$f(x_1, x_2, x_3) = (x_1 - 1)^2 + (x_2 - 3)^2 + 4(x_3 + 5)^2.$$

The subroutines listed are appropriate for this problem. The minimum is clearly 0 when $x_1 = 1$, $x_2 = 3$ and $x_3 = -5$. With initial point $(4, -1, 2)$ and initial step length 4 the program found the minimum after 11 searches. The output is given.

```
        STEEPEST DESCENT
Z=F(X1,X2...XN) AT 2ØØØ
PARTIAL DERIVATIVES G(1),G(2)...G(N) AT 3ØØØ-
 LINEAR SEARCHES BY QUADRATIC INTERPOLATION
NO. OF VARIABLES     3
INITIAL POINT        4,-1,2
INITIAL STEP         4
       CURRENT VALUES
X 1 = 3.232205
X 2 = .Ø237266683
X 3 =-5.166Ø8668

F= 13.9512812

X 1 = 1.1893839
X 2 = 2.74748813
X 3 =-4.5581Ø422

F= .88Ø716Ø34

X 1 = 1.14Ø91457
X 2 = 2.81211391
X 3 =-5.Ø1Ø48472

F= .Ø555978136

X 1 = 1.Ø1195542
X 2 = 2.984Ø5944
X 3 =-4.9721Ø4Ø2

F= 3.5Ø97766E-Ø3

X 1 = 1.ØØ889565
X 2 = 2.98813914
X 3 =-5.ØØØ66188

F= 2.215650Ø25E-Ø4

X 1 = 1.ØØØ75472
X 2 = 2.99899371
X 3 =-4.99823898

F= 1.39859299E-Ø5

X 1 = 1.ØØØ56156
X 2 = 2.99925125
X 3 =-5.ØØØØ4178

F= 8.82963634E-Ø7

X 1 = 1.ØØØØ4764
X 2 = 2.99993648
X 3 =-4.99988884

F= 5.57345Ø73E-Ø8

X 1 = 1.ØØØØ3545
X 2 = 2.99995274
X 3 =-5.ØØØØØ264

F= 3.518Ø887E-Ø9

X 1 = 1.ØØØØØ3Ø1
X 2 = 2.99999599
```

```
X 3 =-4.99999298

F= 2.22Ø55621E-1Ø

X 1 = 1.ØØØØØ224
X 2 = 2.999997Ø2
X 3 =-5.ØØØØØØ17

F= 1.4Ø2Ø3458E-11


        FINAL SOLUTION
X 1 = 1.ØØØØØ224
X 2 = 2.999997Ø2
X 3 =-5.ØØØØØØ17
MINIMUM OF F(X1,X2,...XN)= 1.4Ø2Ø3458E-11
```

The criterion for terminating each search is given at line 8ØØ. Experience has shown that it is not always economic to do the linear search thoroughly. All that is necessary is that we obtain a reduction in the function value from $f(\mathbf{x}_i)$. Thus it might be better to change line 8ØØ to

8ØØ IF FF(1) < ZZ THEN GO TO 1ØØØ.

At first sight this may seem rather crude. The computation to find the minimum in this direction accurately might be considerable. Practical experience with these types of problem shows that it is just not worthwhile. What we lose on the 'accuracy swings' at this stage we make up for on the 'progress to the minimum via changes in direction roundabouts'. This amendment was made to deal with Example 2.

Example 2

Find the minimum of $f(x_1, x_2, x_3) = (x_1 - 1)^4 + (x_2 - 3)^2 + 4(x_3 + 5)^4$.

Again the solution is clearly 0 at (1, 3, −5). The output with initial point (4, 2, −1) with step length 4 is given. Nine searches were needed to find the solution as given.

```
        STEEPEST DESCENT
Z=F(X1,X2...XN) AT 2ØØØ
PARTIAL DERIVATIVES G(1),G(2)...G(N) AT 3ØØØ-
 LINEAR SEARCHES BY QUADRATIC INTERPOLATION
NO. OF VARIABLES      3
INITIAL POINT         4,2,-1
INITIAL STEP          4
        CURRENT VALUES
X 1 = 3.56967284
X 2 = 2.ØØ7969Ø2
X 3 =-5.Ø8Ø139Ø2

F= 44.586785

X 1 = .737139829
X 2 = 2.Ø9Ø77Ø24
X 3 =-5.Ø7979536

F= .831635114

X 1 = .7735Ø3553
X 2 = 3.ØØØ97194
X 3 =-5.Ø7572637
```

```
F= 2.76423752E-Ø3

X 1 = 1.Ø1642718
X 2 = 2.99Ø81194
X 3 =-5.Ø3941129

F= 9.41435872E-Ø5

X 1 = 1.Ø1641829
X 2 = 3.ØØØØ2122
X 3 =-5.Ø3892Ø44

F= 9.25159519E-Ø6

X 1 = 1.Ø1532148
X 2 = 2.99739153
X 3 =-4.98Ø47638

F= 7.44Ø37791E-Ø6

X 1 = 1.Ø1531428
X 2 = 3.ØØØØØ135
X 3 =-4.98Ø53595

F= 6.29111827E-Ø7

X 1 = 1.Ø1341678
X 2 = 2.99964389
X 3 =-4.996119

F= 1.6Ø123934E-Ø7

X 1 = 1.Ø1341195
X 2 = 3.ØØØØØØØ7
X 3 =-4.99611947

F= 3.3263982E-Ø8


          FINAL SOLUTION
X 1 = 1.Ø1341195
X 2 = 3.ØØØØØØØ7
X 3 =-4.99611947
MINIMUM OF F(X1,X2...XN)= 3.3263982E-Ø8
```

Perhaps at this stage a caution should be given concerning the programs. On the face of it, it appears that all that is necessary is to change the subroutines for the function and gradient calculations. Would that things were that easy. There is to date no such thing as the 'universal optimiser' that can be guaranteed under all circumstances. The programs given are robust but care needs to be exercised in their application. They may fail on occasion and the device of changing the termination criterion slightly (from $<0{\cdot}000\,01$ to $<0{\cdot}0001$ for example) may make all the difference. If more accuracy than the machine can give is demanded the program might loop infinitely. This is true of all the programs, so do be prepared to persevere with them in some cases.

Having said that, the method of steepest descent is NOT recommended as a serious optimisation procedure. It has an intuitive appeal but in practice it is far too slow. The point is that the steepest descent property is only a *local* property, and so, frequent changes of direction are necessary with it, and this leads to an inefficient computing procedure. It fails to take any account of the second derivatives.

The best way to do this is to develop methods which are based on quadratic functions. This is the simplest type of function and of course if we use the Taylor series expansion (equation 1.4) we notice that in the vicinity of its minimum any function can be approximated by a quadratic function (unless all its second derivatives are zero). Thus, methods based on procedures that work for quadratic functions should on the face of it stand a good chance of being successful with other functions.

In the next section we develop some of the important properties of the quadratic function of n variables.

4.2 Quadratic Functions

The quadratic function

$$F(\mathbf{x}) = a + \mathbf{x}^{\mathrm{T}}\mathbf{b} + \tfrac{1}{2}\mathbf{x}^{\mathrm{T}}\mathbf{G}\mathbf{x} \tag{4.13}$$

where a is a constant, $\mathbf{b}$ is a constant vector and $\mathbf{G}$ is a positive definite symmetric matrix has a minimum at the point $\mathbf{x}^*$ where $\mathbf{x}^*$ is given by,

$$\begin{aligned} \nabla F(\mathbf{x}^*) &= \mathbf{b} + \mathbf{G}\mathbf{x}^* = \mathbf{0}, \\ \text{i.e.} \quad \mathbf{x}^* &= -\mathbf{G}^{-1}\mathbf{b}. \end{aligned} \tag{4.14}$$

Now we have seen (equation 1.4) that subject to certain continuity conditions any function can be approximated in the region of a point $\mathbf{x}_0$ by

$$\phi(\mathbf{x}) = f(\mathbf{x}_0) + (\mathbf{x} - \mathbf{x}_0)^{\mathrm{T}}\nabla f(\mathbf{x}_0) + \tfrac{1}{2}(\mathbf{x} - \mathbf{x}_0)^{\mathrm{T}}\mathbf{G}(\mathbf{x}_0)(\mathbf{x} - \mathbf{x}_0) \tag{4.15}$$

where $\mathbf{G}(\mathbf{x}_0)$ is the Hessian matrix at $\mathbf{x}_0$.

A reasonable approximation to the minimum for $f(\mathbf{x})$ might be the minimum for $\phi(\mathbf{x})$. If the latter is at $\mathbf{x}_m$ we shall have

$$\nabla f(\mathbf{x}_0) + \mathbf{G}(\mathbf{x}_0)(\mathbf{x}_m - \mathbf{x}_0) = \mathbf{0},$$

$$\therefore \quad \mathbf{x}_m = \mathbf{x}_0 - \mathbf{G}^{-1}(\mathbf{x}_0)\,\nabla f(\mathbf{x}_0),$$

or

$$\mathbf{x}_m = \mathbf{x}_0 - \mathbf{G}^{-1}(\mathbf{x}_0)\,\mathbf{g}(\mathbf{x}_0), \tag{4.16}$$

Thus it appears that we should modify the iterative equation (4.9), and from a point $\mathbf{x}_i$ our next approximation to the minimum should be,

$$\mathbf{x}_{i+1} = \mathbf{x}_i - \mathbf{G}^{-1}(\mathbf{x}_i)\,\mathbf{g}(\mathbf{x}_i) \tag{4.17}$$

or more flexibly,

$$\mathbf{x}_{i+1} = \mathbf{x}_i - \lambda_i\,\mathbf{G}^{-1}(\mathbf{x}_i)\,\mathbf{g}(\mathbf{x}_i) \tag{4.18}$$

where λ_i is determined by a search in the direction $\mathbf{G}^{-1}(\mathbf{x}_i)\,\mathbf{g}(\mathbf{x}_i)$.

The Newton–Raphson method is based on this last equation. We shall not consider it in detail but shall mention some features of it. As they stand equations 4.17 and 4.18 call for the evaluation and inversion of the Hessian matrix at each step and this can be a major computation. If $\mathbf{x}_i$ is close to $\mathbf{x}^*$ the convergence is fast since in general $\phi(\mathbf{x})$ will be a good approximation to $f(\mathbf{x})$ in this region. Both $|\mathbf{g}(\mathbf{x}_{i+1})|$ and $|\mathbf{x}_{i+1} - \mathbf{x}_i|$ should be checked as termination criteria. It is interesting to note that in contrast to the naive steepest descent, our search direction is not $-\mathbf{g}(\mathbf{x}_i)$, but $-\mathbf{G}^{-1}(\mathbf{x}_i)\,\mathbf{g}(\mathbf{x}_i)$ if second derivatives are taken into account. The Davidon–Fletcher–Powell method tries to get the best of all worlds by searching in the direction $-\mathbf{H}_i\,\mathbf{g}(\mathbf{x}_i)$ at the ith stage, where $\mathbf{H}_i$ is a positive definite symmetric matrix which eventually equals $-\mathbf{G}^{-1}(\mathbf{x}^*)$. In this way it sidesteps both the evaluation and inversion of $\mathbf{G}(\mathbf{x}_i)$ at each step.

The direction of search at each stage is thus a crucial factor in the efficiency of iterative search methods. At any stage we want to make our next search in the 'best' direction. For a quadratic function of n variables such as equation 4.13, the best direction in a certain sense is in a direction that is *conjugate* to the previous search directions. We first define this concept and then explain its usefulness.

Two directions $\mathbf{p}$ and $\mathbf{q}$ are said to be conjugate with respect to the symmetric positive definite matrix $\mathbf{G}$ if

$$\mathbf{p}^{\mathrm{T}}\,\mathbf{G}\mathbf{q} = 0. \tag{4.19}$$

We can show from this definition that if $\mathbf{p}_0, \mathbf{p}_1, \mathbf{p}_2, \ldots, \mathbf{p}_{n-1}$ are n mutually conjugate directions in n dimensional space then they are linearly independent. For, if not, there will exist constants $\alpha_0, \alpha_1, \ldots, \alpha_{n-1}$, not all zero, such that,

$$\alpha_0\,\mathbf{p}_0 + \alpha_1\,\mathbf{p}_1 + \cdots + \alpha_{n-1}\,\mathbf{p}_{n-1} = 0.$$

Then for any k $(0 \leqslant k \leqslant n-1)$,

$$\mathbf{p}_k^{\mathrm{T}}\,\mathbf{G} \sum_{j=0}^{n-1} \alpha_j\,\mathbf{p}_j = 0.$$

$$\therefore \quad \alpha_k\,\mathbf{p}_k^{\mathrm{T}}\,\mathbf{G}\mathbf{p}_k = 0,$$

since all other terms vanish ($\mathbf{p}_k^{\mathrm{T}}\,\mathbf{G}\mathbf{p}_j = 0$, $k \neq j$) because of the mutual conjugacy.

Thus since $\mathbf{p}_k \neq \mathbf{0}$ and $\mathbf{G}$ is positive definite

$$\alpha_k = 0.$$

It follows that $\mathbf{p}_0, \mathbf{p}_1, \ldots, \mathbf{p}_{n-1}$ are linearly independent.

Before proceeding it is convenient to rewrite equation 4.13

$$F(\mathbf{x}) = a + \mathbf{x}^{\mathrm{T}}\,\mathbf{b} + \tfrac{1}{2}\mathbf{x}^{\mathrm{T}}\,\mathbf{G}\mathbf{x}$$

which has its optimum at

$$\mathbf{x}^* = -\mathbf{G}^{-1}\,\mathbf{b}$$

as

$$\begin{aligned}
F(\mathbf{x}) &= F(\mathbf{x}^*) + (\mathbf{x} - \mathbf{x}^*)^{\mathrm{T}}\,\nabla F(\mathbf{x}^*) + \tfrac{1}{2}(\mathbf{x} - \mathbf{x}^*)^{\mathrm{T}}\,\mathbf{G}(\mathbf{x} - \mathbf{x}^*) \\
&= F(\mathbf{x}^*) + \tfrac{1}{2}(\mathbf{x} - \mathbf{x}^*)^{\mathrm{T}}\,\mathbf{G}(\mathbf{x} - \mathbf{x}^*) \text{ (since } \nabla F(\mathbf{x}^*) = \mathbf{0}) \\
&= a + \mathbf{x}^{*\mathrm{T}}\,\mathbf{b} + \tfrac{1}{2}\mathbf{x}^{*\mathrm{T}}\,\mathbf{G}\mathbf{x}^* + \tfrac{1}{2}(\mathbf{x} - \mathbf{x}^*)^{\mathrm{T}}\,\mathbf{G}(\mathbf{x} - \mathbf{x}^*) \\
&= a - \tfrac{1}{2}\mathbf{b}^{\mathrm{T}}\,\mathbf{G}^{-1}\,\mathbf{b} + \tfrac{1}{2}(\mathbf{x} - \mathbf{x}^*)\,\mathbf{G}(\mathbf{x} - \mathbf{x}^*)
\end{aligned}$$

$$\text{i.e.} \quad F(\mathbf{x}) = c + \tfrac{1}{2}(\mathbf{x} - \mathbf{x}^*)^{\mathrm{T}}\,\mathbf{G}(\mathbf{x} - \mathbf{x}^*) \tag{4.20}$$

where

$$c = a - \tfrac{1}{2}\mathbf{b}^{\mathrm{T}}\,\mathbf{G}^{-1}\,\mathbf{b} \text{ is a constant.}$$

Suppose we use an iterative search technique to find the minimum of equation 4.20. It is clear that we should not decide on the search directions at the outset (alternating variable search for example) but rather should allow the knowledge gained by earlier searches to determine subsequent directions.

We start at $\mathbf{x}_0$ and search in the direction $\mathbf{p}_0$ to find the minimum at

$$\mathbf{x}_1 = \mathbf{x}_0 + \lambda_0\,\mathbf{p}_0 \tag{4.21}$$

where λ_0 is some scalar.

Note that at $\mathbf{x}_1$, $\mathbf{g}(\mathbf{x}_1) = \nabla F(\mathbf{x}_1)$ is orthogonal to $\mathbf{p}_0$,

$$\mathbf{g}(\mathbf{x}_1)^{\mathrm{T}}\,\mathbf{p}_0 = 0. \tag{4.22}$$

See equations 2.16 and 4.12.

In general at step i we search from a point $\mathbf{x}_i$ in the direction $\mathbf{p}_i$ to find the minimum in this direction at

$$\mathbf{x}_{i+1} = \mathbf{x}_i + \lambda_i\,\mathbf{p}_i \tag{4.23}$$

where

$$\mathbf{g}(\mathbf{x}_{i+1})^{\mathrm{T}}\,\mathbf{p}_i = 0. \tag{4.24}$$

$$\mathbf{g}(\mathbf{x}_i) = \mathbf{G}(\mathbf{x}_i - \mathbf{x}^*) \tag{4.25}$$

for $F(\mathbf{x})$.

By repeated use of equation 4.23 we obtain after n steps.

$$\begin{aligned}\mathbf{x}_n &= \mathbf{x}_{n-1} + \lambda_{n-1}\,\mathbf{p}_{n-1}\\ &= \mathbf{x}_{n-2} + \lambda_{n-2}\,\mathbf{p}_{n-2} + \lambda_{n-1}\,\mathbf{p}_{n-1}\\ &= \mathbf{x}_{j+1} + \sum_{i=j+1}^{n-1} \lambda_i\,\mathbf{p}_i\end{aligned} \tag{4.26}$$

for all j in $0 \leqslant j < n-1$.

Thus from equation 4.25

$$G(\mathbf{x}_n - \mathbf{x}^*) = \mathbf{G}(\mathbf{x}_{j+1} - \mathbf{x}^*) + \sum_{i=j+1}^{n-1} \lambda_i\,\mathbf{G}\mathbf{p}_i. \tag{4.27}$$

Thus

$$\mathbf{g}(\mathbf{x}_n)^{\mathrm{T}}\,\mathbf{p}_j = \mathbf{g}(\mathbf{x}_{j+1})^{\mathrm{T}}\,\mathbf{p}_j + \sum_{i=j+1}^{n-1} \lambda_i\,\mathbf{p}_i^{\mathrm{T}}\,\mathbf{G}\mathbf{p}_j \tag{4.28}$$

and so from equation 4.28

$$\mathbf{g}(\mathbf{x}_n)^{\mathrm{T}}\,\mathbf{p}_j = \sum_{i=j+1}^{n-1} \lambda_i\,\mathbf{p}_i^{\mathrm{T}}\,\mathbf{G}\mathbf{p}_j. \tag{4.29}$$

Now if all the vectors $\mathbf{p}_0, \mathbf{p}_1, \mathbf{p}_2, \ldots, \mathbf{p}_{n-1}$ are mutually conjugate so that

$$\mathbf{p}_i^{\mathrm{T}}\,\mathbf{G}\mathbf{p}_j = 0 \quad \text{for } i \neq j. \tag{4.30}$$

then

$$\mathbf{g}(\mathbf{x}_n)^{\mathrm{T}}\,\mathbf{p}_j = 0, \tag{4.31}$$

for all $j, j = 0, 1, \ldots, n-1$. (It is true for $j = n-1$ from equation 4.24).

But since in this case the $\mathbf{p}_0, \mathbf{p}_1, \ldots, \mathbf{p}_{n-1}$ are linearly independent and so form a basis it follows that

$$\mathbf{g}(\mathbf{x}_n) = \mathbf{0}, \tag{4.32}$$

whence

$$\begin{gathered}\mathbf{G}(\mathbf{x}_n - \mathbf{x}^*) = \mathbf{0}\\ \text{i.e.}\quad \mathbf{x}_n = \mathbf{x}^*.\end{gathered} \tag{4.33}$$

It follows from this that if our searches are carried out in mutually conjugate directions we shall find the minimum of a quadratic function of n variables in at most n steps.

The Fletcher–Reeves method of Section 4.4 seeks to exploit this idea. We shall see however that it is pertinent to the Davidon–Fletcher–Powell method of the next section.

4.3 The Davidon–Fletcher–Powell Method

The Davidon–Fletcher–Powell (D.F.P.) method is based on equations 4.16 and 4.18, although it avoids calculating the inverse Hessian $\mathbf{G}^{-1}(\mathbf{x}_i)$ at each step by setting the search direction at stage i as $-\mathbf{H}_i\,\mathbf{g}(\mathbf{x}_i)$, where $\mathbf{H}_i$ is a positive definite symmetric matrix which is *updated* at each stage in a manner that will be explained later. Ultimately $\mathbf{H}$ becomes equal to the inverse Hessian.

We start with an initial point $\mathbf{x}_0$ and an initial matrix $\mathbf{H}_0$, usually the unit matrix, although any symmetric positive definite matrix will do. The iterative procedure which will be justified shortly proceeds as follows. [N.B. It is convenient to write $\mathbf{g}(\mathbf{x}_i)$ as $\mathbf{g}_i$.]

1 At stage i we have a point $\mathbf{x}_i$ and a positive definite symmetric matrix $\mathbf{H}_i$.
2 Set the direction of search

$$\mathbf{d}_i = -\mathbf{H}_i\,\mathbf{g}_i. \tag{4.34}$$

3 Carry out a linear search on the line $\mathbf{x}_i + \lambda\mathbf{d}_i$ to find the value λ_i which minimises $f(\mathbf{x}_i + \lambda_i\mathbf{d}_i)$.
4 Put

$$\mathbf{v}_i = \lambda_i\,\mathbf{d}_i. \tag{4.35}$$

5 Put

$$\mathbf{x}_{i+1} = \mathbf{x}_i + \mathbf{v}_i. \tag{4.36}$$

6 Find $f(\mathbf{x}_{i+1})$ and $\mathbf{g}_{i+1}$. Terminate the procedure if $|\mathbf{g}_{i+1}|$ or $|\mathbf{v}_i|$ are sufficiently small. Otherwise proceed.
N.B. From equation 4.24

$$\mathbf{g}_{i+1}^{\mathrm{T}}\,\mathbf{v}_i = 0. \tag{4.37}$$

7 Put

$$\mathbf{u}_i = \mathbf{g}_{i+1} - \mathbf{g}_i. \tag{4.38}$$

8 Update the $\mathbf{H}$ matrix by

$$\mathbf{H}_{i+1} = \mathbf{H}_i + \mathbf{A}_i + \mathbf{B}_i \tag{4.39}$$

where

$$\mathbf{A}_i = \mathbf{v}_i \mathbf{v}_i^T/(\mathbf{v}_i^T \mathbf{u}_i) \tag{4.40}$$

$$\mathbf{B}_i = -\mathbf{H}_i \mathbf{u}_i \mathbf{u}_i^T \mathbf{H}_i/(\mathbf{u}_i^T \mathbf{H}_i \mathbf{u}_i). \tag{4.41}$$

9 Increase i to $i + 1$ and return to step 2.

We shall justify the procedure following the arguments of Fletcher and Powell.

(a) The process is stable, $\mathbf{v}_i$ is downhill and λ_i is positive. Since $\mathbf{g}_i$ is the direction of steepest ascent, $\mathbf{v}_i$ will be downhill if and only if

$$\begin{aligned} -\mathbf{v}_i^T \mathbf{g}_i &= -\mathbf{g}_i^T \mathbf{v}_i \\ &= \lambda_i \mathbf{g}_i^T \mathbf{H}_i \mathbf{g}_i \end{aligned} \tag{4.42}$$

is positive.

This will be so if $\mathbf{H}_i$ is symmetric positive definite for all i. $\mathbf{H}_0$ has these properties by assumption. The updating at equations 4.39, 4.40 and 4.41 maintains the symmetry. We prove that $\mathbf{H}_i$ remains positive definite by induction.

Thus assume $\mathbf{H}_i$ is symmetric positive definite. Then it has a square root $\mathbf{C}_i$ such that

$$\mathbf{C}_i^T \mathbf{C}_i = \mathbf{C}_i \mathbf{C}_i^T = \mathbf{H}_i. \tag{4.43}$$

Put

$$\mathbf{p} = \mathbf{C}_i \boldsymbol{\eta} \quad \text{and} \quad \mathbf{q} = \mathbf{C}_i \mathbf{u}_i \tag{4.44}$$

where $\boldsymbol{\eta}$ is any vector.

Then

$$\begin{aligned} \boldsymbol{\eta}^T \mathbf{H}_{i+1} \boldsymbol{\eta} &= \boldsymbol{\eta}^T \mathbf{H}_i \boldsymbol{\eta} + \frac{\boldsymbol{\eta}^T \mathbf{v}_i \mathbf{v}_i^T \boldsymbol{\eta}}{\mathbf{v}_i^T \mathbf{u}_i} - \frac{\boldsymbol{\eta}^T \mathbf{H}_i \mathbf{u}_i \mathbf{u}_i^T \mathbf{H}_i \boldsymbol{\eta}}{\mathbf{u}_i^T \mathbf{H}_i \mathbf{u}_i} \\ &= p^2 - \frac{(\mathbf{p}^T \mathbf{q})^2}{q^2} + \frac{(\boldsymbol{\eta}^T \mathbf{v}_i)^2}{\mathbf{v}_i^T \mathbf{u}_i} \\ &= \frac{p^2 q^2 - (\mathbf{p}^T \mathbf{q})^2}{q^2} + \frac{(\boldsymbol{\eta}^T \mathbf{v}_i)^2}{\mathbf{v}_i^T \mathbf{u}_i} \\ &\geqslant \frac{(\boldsymbol{\eta}^T \mathbf{v}_i)^2}{\mathbf{v}_i^T \mathbf{u}_i} \end{aligned} \tag{4.45}$$

because $\mathbf{p}^2 \mathbf{q}^2 \geqslant (\mathbf{p}^T \mathbf{q})^2$ by the Schwarz inequality.

Now the denominator of equation 4.45 is positive because

$$\begin{aligned} \mathbf{v}_i^T \mathbf{u}_i &= \mathbf{v}_i^T [\mathbf{g}_{i+1} - \mathbf{g}_i] \\ &= -\mathbf{v}_i^T \mathbf{g}_i \quad \text{since } \mathbf{v}_i^T \mathbf{g}_{i+1} = 0 \text{ from equation 4.37} \\ &= \lambda_i \mathbf{g}_i^T \mathbf{H}_i \mathbf{g}_i \\ &> 0 \quad \text{because } \lambda_i > 0 \text{ and } \mathbf{H}_i \text{ is positive definite.} \end{aligned} \tag{4.46}$$

Thus $\boldsymbol{\eta}^T \mathbf{H}_{i+1} \boldsymbol{\eta} > 0$ which proves $\mathbf{H}_{i+1}$ to be positive definite. Thus the induction proof is complete.

(b) We next show that if the D.F.P. method is applied to the quadratic function (equation 4.13) with $\mathbf{G}$ symmetric positive definite, then $\mathbf{H}_n = \mathbf{G}^{-1}$ and the process will terminate after n stages. We do this by showing that $\mathbf{v}_0, \mathbf{v}_1, \ldots, \mathbf{v}_k$ are linearly independent eigenvectors of $\mathbf{H}_{k+1}\mathbf{G}$ with eigenvalue 1. Thus $\mathbf{H}_n \mathbf{G}$ must be the unit matrix.

We note from equation 4.38 that

$$\begin{aligned} \mathbf{u}_i &= \mathbf{g}_{i+1} - \mathbf{g}_i \\ &= \mathbf{G}\mathbf{x}_{i+1} - \mathbf{G}\mathbf{x}_i \\ &= \mathbf{G}\mathbf{v}_i. \end{aligned} \tag{4.47}$$

Also

$$\begin{aligned} \mathbf{H}_{i+1}\mathbf{G}\mathbf{v}_i &= \mathbf{H}_{i+1}\mathbf{u}_i \quad \text{(from equation 4.47)} \\ &= \mathbf{H}_i\mathbf{u}_i + \mathbf{A}_i\mathbf{u}_i + \mathbf{B}_i\mathbf{u}_i \\ &= \mathbf{H}_i\mathbf{u}_i + \mathbf{v}_i - \mathbf{H}_i\mathbf{u} \end{aligned}$$

using equations 4.39, 4.40 and 4.41 and noting that $\mathbf{v}_i^T\mathbf{u}_i$ and $\mathbf{u}_i^T\mathbf{H}_i\mathbf{u}_i$ are scalars which can be cancelled.

Thus

$$\mathbf{H}_{i+1}\mathbf{G}\mathbf{v}_i = \mathbf{v}_i. \tag{4.48}$$

We next show that for $k = 2, 3, \ldots, n$

$$\mathbf{v}_i^T\mathbf{G}\mathbf{v}_j = 0, \quad 0 \leqslant i < j < k \tag{4.49}$$

$$\mathbf{H}_k\mathbf{G}\mathbf{v}_i = \mathbf{v}_i, \quad 0 \leqslant i < k \tag{4.50}$$

We do this by induction on k. If we put $i = 0$ in equation 4.48 we obtain $\mathbf{H}_1\mathbf{G}\mathbf{v}_0 = \mathbf{v}_0$ which is equation 4.50 when $k = 1$. Equations 4.50 with $k = 2$ are

$$\mathbf{H}_2\mathbf{G}\mathbf{v}_0 = \mathbf{v}_0 \quad \text{and} \quad \mathbf{H}_2\mathbf{G}\mathbf{v}_1 = \mathbf{v}_1.$$

The second of these comes from equation 4.48 with $i = 1$.

For the first

$$\mathbf{H}_2\mathbf{G}\mathbf{v}_0 = \mathbf{H}_1\mathbf{G}\mathbf{v}_0 + \mathbf{v}_1\frac{\mathbf{v}_1^T\mathbf{G}\mathbf{v}_0}{\mathbf{v}_1^T\mathbf{u}_1} - \frac{\mathbf{H}_1\mathbf{u}_1\mathbf{u}_1^T\mathbf{H}_1\mathbf{G}\mathbf{v}_0}{\mathbf{u}_1^T\mathbf{H}_1\mathbf{u}_1}$$

The last two terms on the right are both zero since

$$\begin{aligned} \mathbf{v}_1^T\mathbf{G}\mathbf{v}_0 = \mathbf{v}_0^T\mathbf{G}\mathbf{v}_1 &= \mathbf{v}_o^T\mathbf{G}(-\lambda_1\mathbf{H}_1\mathbf{g}_1) \\ &= -\lambda_1\mathbf{g}_1^T\mathbf{H}_1\mathbf{G}\mathbf{v}_0 \\ &= -\lambda_1\mathbf{g}_1^T\mathbf{v}_0 \quad \text{(from equation 4.48 with } i = 0) \\ &= 0 \quad \text{(from equation 4.37 with } i = 0). \end{aligned}$$

Also $\mathbf{u}_1 = \mathbf{G}\mathbf{v}_1$, so that $\mathbf{u}_1^T\mathbf{H}_1\mathbf{G}\mathbf{v}_0 = \mathbf{v}_1^T\mathbf{G}\mathbf{v}_0$. Thus equations 4.50 are shown to be true for $k = 2$ and the result just established, when transposed gives

$$\mathbf{v}_0^T\mathbf{G}\mathbf{v}_1 = 0$$

which is equation 4.49 when $k = 2$.

We now proceed with the induction and try to show that if equations 4.49 and 4.50 are true for values up to k they are also true for values up to $k + 1$.

We have

$$\begin{aligned} \mathbf{g}_k &= \mathbf{b} + \mathbf{G}\mathbf{x}_k \\ &= \mathbf{b} + \mathbf{G}(\mathbf{x}_{k-1} + \mathbf{v}_{k-1}) \\ &= \mathbf{b} + \mathbf{G}(\mathbf{x}_{k-2} + \mathbf{v}_{k-2} + \mathbf{v}_{k-1}) \text{ etc.} \\ &= \mathbf{g}_{i+1} + \mathbf{G}(\mathbf{v}_{i+1} + \mathbf{v}_{i+2} + \cdots + \mathbf{v}_{k-1}). \end{aligned} \tag{4.51}$$

Thus from equation 4.49, when $i < k - 1$

$$\mathbf{v}_i^{\mathrm{T}} \mathbf{g}_k = \mathbf{v}_i^{\mathrm{T}} \mathbf{g}_{i+1} = 0 \quad \text{by equation 4.37}$$

and from equation 4.37 directly

$$\mathbf{v}_{k-1}^{\mathrm{T}} \mathbf{g}_k = 0.$$

Thus

$$\mathbf{v}_i^{\mathrm{T}} \mathbf{g}_k = 0, \quad 0 \leqslant i < k, \tag{4.52}$$

so that from equations 4.50

$$\mathbf{v}_i^{\mathrm{T}} \mathbf{G}\mathbf{H}_k \mathbf{g}_k = 0 \quad 0 \leqslant i < k$$

so that

$$-\mathbf{v}_i^{\mathrm{T}} \mathbf{G}\mathbf{d}_k = 0$$

so that

$$-\mathbf{v}_i^{\mathrm{T}} \mathbf{G}\mathbf{v}_k = 0 \quad \text{since } \mathbf{v}_k = \lambda_k \mathbf{d}_k.$$

Thus we have established that

$$\mathbf{v}_i^{\mathrm{T}} \mathbf{G}\mathbf{v}_k = 0 \quad \text{for } 0 \leqslant i < k \tag{4.53}$$

$$\text{i.e.} \quad \mathbf{v}_i^{\mathrm{T}} \mathbf{G}\mathbf{v}_j = 0 \quad \text{for } 0 \leqslant i < j < k + 1. \tag{4.54}$$

We also have from equations 4.47 and 4.50

$$\begin{aligned} (\mathbf{u}_k)^{\mathrm{T}} \mathbf{H}_k \mathbf{G}\mathbf{v}_i &= \mathbf{u}_k^{\mathrm{T}} \mathbf{v}_i \\ &= \mathbf{v}_k^{\mathrm{T}} \mathbf{G}\mathbf{v}_i = 0 \quad \text{for } 0 \leqslant i < k\ (<k + 1). \end{aligned} \tag{4.55}$$

Hence from equations 4.39, 4.40, 4.41, 4.50

$$\begin{aligned} \mathbf{H}_{k+1} \mathbf{G}\mathbf{v}_i &= \mathbf{H}_k \mathbf{G}\mathbf{v}_i + \frac{\mathbf{v}_k \mathbf{v}_k^{\mathrm{T}} \mathbf{G}\mathbf{v}_i}{\mathbf{v}_k^{\mathrm{T}} \mathbf{u}_k} - \frac{\mathbf{H}_k \mathbf{u}_k \mathbf{u}_k^{\mathrm{T}} \mathbf{H}_k \mathbf{G}\mathbf{v}_i}{\mathbf{u}_k^{\mathrm{T}} \mathbf{H}_k \mathbf{u}_k} \\ &= \mathbf{H}_k \mathbf{G}\mathbf{v}_i, \end{aligned}$$

since

$$\mathbf{v}_k^{\mathrm{T}} \mathbf{G}\mathbf{v}_i = 0$$

and

$$\mathbf{u}_k^{\mathrm{T}} \mathbf{H}_k \mathbf{G}\mathbf{v}_i = \mathbf{u}_k^{\mathrm{T}} \mathbf{v}_i$$
$$= \mathbf{v}_k^{\mathrm{T}} \mathbf{G}\mathbf{v}_i = 0 \quad \text{for } 0 \leqslant i < k.$$

Thus we have shown that

$$\mathbf{H}_{k+1} \mathbf{G}\mathbf{v}_i = \mathbf{H}_k \mathbf{G}\mathbf{v}_i = \mathbf{v}_i \quad \text{for } 0 \leqslant i < k. \tag{4.56}$$

Also for $i = k$

$$\mathbf{H}_{k+1} \mathbf{G}\mathbf{v}_k = \mathbf{H}_k \mathbf{G}\mathbf{v}_k + \frac{\mathbf{v}_k \mathbf{v}_k^{\mathrm{T}} \mathbf{G}\mathbf{v}_k}{\mathbf{v}_k^{\mathrm{T}} \mathbf{u}_k} - \frac{\mathbf{H}_k \mathbf{u}_k \mathbf{u}_k^{\mathrm{T}} \mathbf{H}_k \mathbf{G}\mathbf{v}_k}{\mathbf{u}_k^{\mathrm{T}} \mathbf{H}_k \mathbf{u}_k}$$
$$= \mathbf{H}_k \mathbf{u}_k + \mathbf{v}_k - \mathbf{H}_k \mathbf{u}_k$$

since

$$\mathbf{v}_k^{\mathrm{T}} \mathbf{G}\mathbf{v}_k = \mathbf{v}_k^{\mathrm{T}} \mathbf{u}_k \quad \text{and} \quad \mathbf{u}_k^{\mathrm{T}} \mathbf{H}_k \mathbf{G}\mathbf{v}_k = \mathbf{u}_k^{\mathrm{T}} \mathbf{H}_k \mathbf{u}_k$$

Thus $\mathbf{H}_{k+1} \mathbf{G}\mathbf{v}_k = \mathbf{v}_k$ and this combined with equation 4.56 gives

$$\mathbf{H}_{k+1} \mathbf{G}\mathbf{v}_i = \mathbf{v}_i \quad 0 \leqslant i < k + 1. \tag{4.57}$$

Equations 4.54 and 4.57 extend equations 4.49 and 4.50 to the next value of k and so complete the induction proof of the latter.

Equation 4.49 shows that $\mathbf{v}_0, \mathbf{v}_1, \ldots, \mathbf{v}_{n-1}$ are linearly independent. They are mutually conjugate with respect to $\mathbf{G}$. From equations 4.50 $\mathbf{v}_0, \mathbf{v}_1, \ldots, \mathbf{v}_{n-1}$ are eigenvectors of $\mathbf{H}_n \mathbf{G}$ with eigenvalue 1. Thus $\mathbf{H}_n \mathbf{G}$ must be a unit matrix.

$$\therefore \quad \mathbf{H}_n = \mathbf{G}^{-1}. \tag{4.58}$$

That the minimum is found by n iterations follows from equation 4.52. $\mathbf{g}_n$ must be orthogonal to each of the n independent vectors $\mathbf{v}_0, \mathbf{v}_1, \ldots, \mathbf{v}_{n-1}$. Thus

$$\mathbf{g}_n = 0. \tag{4.59}$$

(c) The updating of the $\mathbf{H}$ matrix follows equation 4.39.

$$\mathbf{H}_n = \mathbf{H}_0 + \sum_{i=0}^{n-1} \mathbf{A}_i + \sum_{i=0}^{n-1} \mathbf{B}_i.$$

We show that $\mathbf{G}^{-1} = \sum_{i=0}^{n-1} \mathbf{A}_i$. The orthogonality conditions (equation 4.49) imply that

$$\mathbf{V}^{\mathrm{T}} \mathbf{G}\mathbf{V} = \boldsymbol{\Delta}$$

where $\mathbf{V}$ is the matrix of vectors $\mathbf{v}_i$ and $\boldsymbol{\Delta}$ is the diagonal matrix with elements $\mathbf{v}_i^{\mathrm{T}} \mathbf{G}\mathbf{v}_i$.

Thus

$$\mathbf{G} = (\mathbf{V}^{\mathrm{T}})^{-1} \boldsymbol{\Delta} \mathbf{V}^{-1}$$
$$\therefore \quad \mathbf{G}^{-1} = \mathbf{V} \boldsymbol{\Delta}^{-1} \mathbf{V}^{\mathrm{T}}$$

and since Δ is a diagonal matrix we can do the inversion and matrix multiplication to obtain

$$\mathbf{G}^{-1} = \sum_{i=0}^{n-1} \frac{\mathbf{v}_i \mathbf{v}_i^{\mathrm{T}}}{\mathbf{v}_i^{\mathrm{T}} \mathbf{G} \mathbf{v}_i} = \sum_{i=0}^{n-1} \frac{\mathbf{v}_i \mathbf{v}_i^{\mathrm{T}}}{\mathbf{v}_i^{\mathrm{T}} \mathbf{u}_i} \quad \text{by equation 4.47.}$$

Thus

$$\mathbf{G}^{-1} = \sum_{i=0}^{n-1} \mathbf{A}_i. \tag{4.60}$$

Since equation 4.48 must be valid

$$\mathbf{H}_{i+1} \mathbf{G} \mathbf{v}_i = \mathbf{v}_i \quad \text{implies} \quad \mathbf{v}_i = \mathbf{H}_i \mathbf{G} \mathbf{v}_i + \mathbf{A}_i \mathbf{G} \mathbf{v}_i + \mathbf{B}_i \mathbf{G} \mathbf{v}_i.$$

Thus since

$$\mathbf{A}_i \mathbf{G} \mathbf{v}_i = \mathbf{A}_i \mathbf{u}_i = \frac{\mathbf{v}_i \mathbf{v}_i^{\mathrm{T}} \mathbf{u}_i}{\mathbf{v}_i^{\mathrm{T}} \mathbf{u}_i} = \mathbf{v}_i$$

$$\mathbf{B}_i \mathbf{G} \mathbf{v}_i = -\mathbf{H}_i \mathbf{G} \mathbf{v}_i = -\mathbf{H}_i \mathbf{u}_i. \tag{4.61}$$

Thus a simple form (though not necessarily the only form) for $\mathbf{B}_i$ is

$$\mathbf{B}_i = \frac{-\mathbf{H}_i \mathbf{u}_i \mathbf{z}^{\mathrm{T}}}{\mathbf{z}^{\mathrm{T}} \mathbf{G} \mathbf{v}_i} = \frac{-\mathbf{H}_i \mathbf{u}_i \mathbf{z}^{\mathrm{T}}}{\mathbf{z}^{\mathrm{T}} \mathbf{u}_i} \quad \text{where } \mathbf{z} \text{ is any vector.}$$

Since we want $\mathbf{B}_i$ to be symmetric we take $\mathbf{z} = \mathbf{H}_i \mathbf{u}_i$ so that

$$\mathbf{B}_i = \frac{-\mathbf{H}_i \mathbf{u}_i \mathbf{u}_i^{\mathrm{T}} \mathbf{H}_i}{\mathbf{u}_i^{\mathrm{T}} \mathbf{H}_i \mathbf{u}_i}. \tag{4.62}$$

This completes the theory of the D.F.P. method. The method uses both the ideas of the Newton–Raphson method and conjugate directions. When applied to a quadratic function of n variables it converges in at most n iterations. It is a very powerful optimisation procedure and works very efficiently for most functions whether they are quadratic or not.

We give a flow chart of the procedure and a program to implement the method. Subroutines to evaluate the function under consideration and its derivatives have to be written. The underlying logic of the method is contained within the program. The linear searches required are carried out by cubic interpolation and the procedure given is very robust. These searches are not carried out to ultimate convergence but instead an improvement in the function is sought. In theory of course this means that the method loses the convergence properties for quadratic functions. In practice it is still very efficient and rapid. It is doubtful that the extra work involved in carrying out the linear searches completely would be worthwhile.

The program given follows the flow chart, uses the notation given there and has explanatory remarks. The linear searches, lines 6ØØ–1Ø1Ø, use the cubic interpolation routine of Section 2.6 except that they do not follow through to convergence. Thus at 92Ø the program will exit from the search if the interpolated function value is less than both of the values used in the routine. The subsequent search interval if any is decided at line 93Ø.

Example 1

Use (3, −1, 0, 1) as a starting point in order to minimise Powell's function

$$f(x_1, x_2, x_3, x_4) = (x_1 + 10x_2)^2 + 5(x_3 - x_4)^2 + (x_2 - 2x_3)^4 + 10(x_1 - x_4)^4.$$

The subroutines written are correct for this function. The starting point suggested is a particularly awkward one for this function. The minimum is 0 at (0, 0, 0, 0). The way the method proceeds to this value can be seen in the sections of output which are given.

Flow Chart for the Davidon–Fletcher–Powell Method

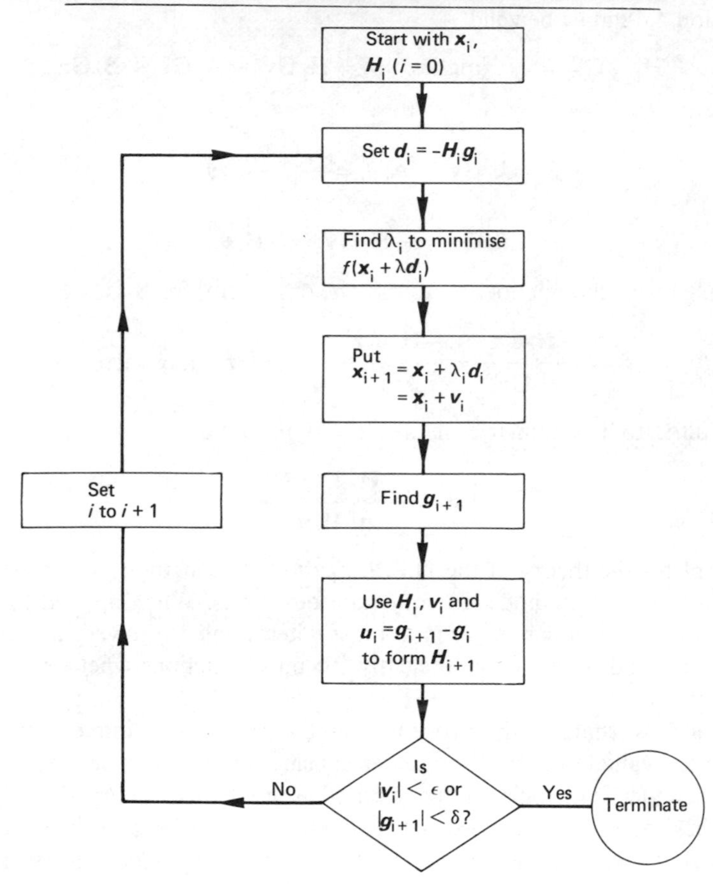


```
READY.

 100 PRINT"MINIMISATION BY D-F-P"
 120 REM LINEAR SEARCHES BY CUBIC INTERPOLATION
 150 REM F(X1,X2...XN) AT 5000;G(1),G(2)...G(N) AT 6000
 200 PRINT"NUMBER OF VARIABLES":INPUT N
 220 DIM X,P,Q,R,D,G,U,V,Y,M(N)
 240 DIM H(N,N)
 300 REM SET H TO UNIT MATRIX INITIALLY
 320 FOR I=1TO N:H(I,I)=1:NEXT I
 330 PRINT"INITIAL VALUES"
 340 FOR I=1TO N:PRINT"X"I,:INPUT X(I):NEXT I:PRINT""
 360 REM INTERMEDIATE OUTPUT
```

```
380 PRINT"         CURRENT VALUES"
400 FOR I=1TO N:P(I)=X(I):Y(I)=X(I):PRINT"X";I,X(I):NEXT I
410 GOSUB 5000
420 PRINT"ITERATION"CC"VALUE"Z
430 FP=Z:GOSUB 6000:G1=G0
440 REM STORE GRADIENT IN U AND SET SEARCH DIRECTION D
450 FOR I=1TO N
460 U(I)=G(I):D(I)=0
470 FOR J=1TO N
480 D(I)=D(I)-H(I,J)*G(J)
490 NEXT J
500 NEXT I
600 GP=0
610 FOR I=1TO N:GP=GP+G(I)*D(I):NEXT I
620 IF GP=0 THEN GOTO 680
625 REM FIND INITIAL STEP AND IF NECESSARY REVERSE DOWNHILL
630 QX=ABS(2*FP/GP):IF QX>1 THEN QX=1
640 FOR I=1TO N
650 X(I)=P(I)-QX*D(I):P(I)=X(I):NEXT I
660 GOSUB 5000:FP=Z:PRINT"INSTABILITY?"
670 GOSUB 6000:G1=G0:GOTO 600
680 QX=ABS(2*FP/GP):IF QX>1 THEN QX=1
690 HH=QX
700 REM FIND NEXT POINT Q
710 BB=HH
720 FOR I=1TO N
730 Q(I)=P(I)+BB*D(I):X(I)=Q(I)
740 NEXT I
750 GOSUB 5000:FQ=Z
760 GOSUB 6000:G2=G0
770 GQ=0
780 FOR I=1TO N
790 GQ=GQ+G(I)*D(I)
800 NEXT I
810 IF GQ>0 OR FQ>FP THEN GOTO 830
815 REM DO CUBIC INTERPOLATION OR DOUBLE STEP TO BRACKET MINIMUM
820 HH=2*HH:GOTO 700
830 ZZ=3*(FP-FQ)/HH:ZZ=ZZ+GP+GQ
840 WW=ZZ*ZZ-GP*GQ:IF WW<0 THEN WW=0
850 W=SQR(WW)
860 DD=HH*(1-(GQ+W-ZZ)/(GQ-GP+2*W))
870 FOR I=1TO N:X(I)=P(I)+DD*D(I):NEXT I
880 GOSUB 5000:FR=Z
890 GOSUB 6000:G3=G0
895 REM FIND GRADIENT AT NEW POINT
900 GR=0
910 FOR I=1TO N:GR=GR+G(I)*D(I):NEXT I
920 IF Z<=FP AND Z<=FQ THEN GOTO 1100
930 IF GR>0 THEN GOTO 990
960 HH=HH-DD
970 FOR I=1TO N:P(I)=X(I):NEXT I
980 FP=Z:GP=GR:G1=G0:GOTO 830
990 HH=DD
1000 FOR I=1TO N:Q(I)=X(I):NEXT I
1010 FQ=Z:GQ=GR:G2=G0:GOTO 830
1050 REM UPDATE THE H MATRIX
1100 KK=0:WK=0:DK=0
1110 FOR I=1TO N
1120 U(I)=G(I)-U(I):V(I)=X(I)-Y(I)
1130 NEXT I
1140 FOR I=1TO N:M(I)=0
1150 FOR J=1TO N
1160 M(I)=M(I)+H(I,J)*U(J)
1170 NEXT J
1180 KK=KK+M(I)*U(I):WK=WK+V(I)*U(I)
```

```
 119Ø DK=DK+V(I)*V(I)
 12ØØ NEXT I
 12Ø5 IF KK=Ø OR WK=Ø THEN GOTO 126Ø
 121Ø FOR I=1TO N
 122Ø FOR J=1TO N
 123Ø H(I,J)=H(I,J)-M(I)*M(J)/KK+V(I)*V(J)/WK
 124Ø NEXT J
 125Ø NEXT I
 126Ø CC=CC+1
 1265 REM TEST FOR TERMINATION
 127Ø IF SQR(DK)<Ø.ØØØØ5 OR G3<Ø.ØØØØ1THEN GOTO 13ØØ
 1275 REM START A NEW SEARCH
 128Ø GOTO 4ØØ
 13ØØ PRINT"MINIMISATION COMPLETE"
 131Ø PRINT"ITERATIONS="CC"VALUE="Z
 132Ø FOR I=1 TO N
 133Ø PRINT"X";I,X(I)
 134Ø NEXT I
 135Ø END
 5ØØØ Z=Ø
 5Ø1Ø Z=(X(1)+1Ø*X(2))↑2+5*(X(3)-X(4))↑2
 5Ø2Ø Z=Z+(X(2)-2*X(3))↑4+1Ø*(X(1)-X(4))↑4
 51ØØ TT=TT+1
 52ØØ RETURN
 6ØØØ GØ=Ø
 61ØØ G(1)=2*(X(1)+1Ø*X(2))+4Ø*(X(1)-X(4))↑3
 62ØØ G(2)=2Ø*(X(1)+1Ø*X(2))+4*(X(2)-2*X(3))↑3
 63ØØ G(3)=1Ø*(X(3)-X(4))-8*(X(2)-2*X(3))↑3
 64ØØ G(4)=-1Ø*(X(3)-X(4))-4Ø*(X(1)-X(4))↑3
 7ØØØ FOR I=1TO N:GØ=GØ+G(I)*G(I):NEXT I
 7Ø1Ø GØ=SQR(GØ)
 75ØØ RETURN
READY.
```

```
MINIMISATION BY D-F-P
NUMBER OF VARIABLES
INITIAL VALUES
X 1   3         X 2  -1           X 3   Ø          X 4   1
        CURRENT VALUES
X 1            3
X 2           -1
X 3            Ø
X 4            1
ITERATION Ø VALUE 215
X 1            1.94987427
X 2           -.5Ø5823188
X 3            6.86346684E-Ø3
X 4            2.Ø6384286
ITERATION 1 VALUE 3Ø.892463
X 1            1.952Ø9394
X 2           -.146Ø42759
X 3            .113912748
X 4            1.9832Ø49
ITERATION 2 VALUE 17.7325487
X 1            1.672Ø8858
X 2           -.132614431
X 3            .617338618
X 4            1.74Ø23851
ITERATION 3 VALUE 9.91939378
X 1            .121277Ø88
X 2           -9.13125985E-Ø3
X 3            .231434374
X 4            .21547Ø374
```

```
ITERATION 4 VALUE .Ø525920218
X 1            .112441564
X 2           -.Ø159242Ø98
X 3            .17549Ø559
X 4            .2Ø5192275
ITERATION 5 VALUE .Ø254637281


X 1            2.63223488E-Ø4
X 2           -2.6Ø51721E-Ø5
X 3            9.8525Ø992E-Ø4
X 4            9.84264Ø15E-Ø4
ITERATION 23 VALUE 3.Ø7875Ø7E-11
X 1            2.39893796E-Ø4
X 2           -2.4Ø57Ø933E-Ø5
X 3            7.84283692E-Ø4
X 4            7.84533113E-Ø4
ITERATION 24 VALUE 8.Ø83Ø6561E-12
X 1            1.959848Ø7E-Ø4
X 2           -1.95466188E-Ø5
X 3            4.36229416E-Ø4
X 4            4.36Ø35Ø74E-Ø4
ITERATION 25 VALUE 1.12411233E-12
MINIMISATION COMPLETE
ITERATIONS= 26 VALUE= 3.Ø4628368E-13
X 1            1.85683677E-Ø4
X 2           -1.858Ø6523E-Ø5
X 3            3.51518478E-Ø4
X 4            3.51564962E-Ø4
```

4.4 The Fletcher–Reeves Method

The Fletcher–Reeves method tries to exploit the fact that for a quadratic function of n variables, n linear searches along *mutually conjugate* directions will locate the minimum.

Consider the function given by equation 4.13, i.e.

$$f(\mathbf{x}) = a + \mathbf{b}^{\mathrm{T}} \mathbf{x} + \tfrac{1}{2}\mathbf{x}^{\mathrm{T}} \mathbf{G}\mathbf{x}.$$

We seek to make our searches along directions which are mutually conjugate with respect to **G**.

Our first search direction from our first point $\mathbf{x}_1$ is made in the direction of steepest descent (which seems reasonable);

$$\mathbf{d}_1 = -\mathbf{g}_1 \tag{4.63}$$

to find the value λ_1 which minimises

$$f(\mathbf{x}_1 + \lambda \mathbf{d}_1).$$

Put

$$\mathbf{x}_2 = \mathbf{x}_1 + \lambda_1 \mathbf{d}_1 \tag{4.64}$$

and search in a direction $\mathbf{d}_2$, conjugate to $\mathbf{d}_1$ (we choose $\mathbf{d}_2$ to be a linear combination of $\mathbf{d}_1$ and $-\mathbf{g}_2$) to find

$$\mathbf{x}_3 = \mathbf{x}_2 + \lambda_2 \mathbf{d}_2 \tag{4.65}$$

to minimise $f(\mathbf{x}_2 + \lambda\mathbf{d}_2)$. The search direction $\mathbf{d}_3$ from $\mathbf{x}_3$ is chosen conjugate to both $\mathbf{d}_1$ and $\mathbf{d}_2$. At the $(k+1)$th stage we choose $\mathbf{d}_{k+1}$ to be a linear combination of $-\mathbf{g}_{k+1}$, $\mathbf{d}_1, \mathbf{d}_2, \ldots, \mathbf{d}_k$ that is conjugate to all of $\mathbf{d}_1, \mathbf{d}_2, \ldots, \mathbf{d}_k$.

Thus $\mathbf{d}_{k+1} = -\mathbf{g}_{k+1} + \sum_{r=1}^{k} \alpha_r \mathbf{d}_r$, $k = 1, 2, \ldots$. It transpires that all the α_r are zero except for α_k and that

$$\mathbf{d}_{k+1} = -\mathbf{g}_{k+1} + \alpha_k \mathbf{d}_k \tag{4.66}$$

and

$$\alpha_k = \mathbf{g}_{k+1}^2/\mathbf{g}_k^2. \tag{4.67}$$

We first establish equations 4.66 and 4.67 for $k = 1$, before proceeding by induction. Since $f(\mathbf{x}_2) = f(\mathbf{x}_1 + \lambda_1 \mathbf{d}_1)$ is the minimum of $f(\mathbf{x}_1 + \lambda\mathbf{d}_1)$ along the line,

$$\mathbf{g}_2^{\mathrm{T}} \mathbf{d}_1 = -\mathbf{g}_2^{\mathrm{T}} \mathbf{g}_1 = 0. \tag{4.68}$$

We have had this result many times before (equations 4.37, 4.22, 4.24), and of course for a quadratic

$$\mathbf{g}_2 = \mathbf{b} + \mathbf{G}\mathbf{x}_2, \quad \mathbf{g}_1 = \mathbf{b} + \mathbf{G}\mathbf{x}_1$$

Thus if $\mathbf{d}_1$ and $\mathbf{d}_2 = -\mathbf{g}_2 + \alpha_1 \mathbf{d}_1$ are conjugate

$$\mathbf{d}_2^{\mathrm{T}} \mathbf{G}\mathbf{d}_1 = 0,$$

$$\text{i.e.} \quad -\mathbf{g}_2^{\mathrm{T}} \mathbf{G}\mathbf{d}_1 + \alpha_1 \mathbf{d}_1^{\mathrm{T}} \mathbf{G}\mathbf{d}_1 = 0$$

$$\therefore \quad \frac{(-\mathbf{g}_2^{\mathrm{T}} - \alpha_1 \mathbf{g}_1^{\mathrm{T}})\, \mathbf{G}(\mathbf{x}_2 - \mathbf{x}_1)}{\lambda_1} = 0.$$

$$\therefore \quad (-\mathbf{g}_2^{\mathrm{T}} - \alpha\mathbf{g}_1^{\mathrm{T}})(\mathbf{g}_2 - \mathbf{g}_1) = 0$$

$$\therefore \quad -\mathbf{g}_2^2 + \alpha_1 \mathbf{g}_1^2 = 0,$$

the other terms vanishing from equation 4.68.

$$\therefore \quad \alpha_1 = \mathbf{g}_2^2/\mathbf{g}_1^2$$

as required. This is just equation 4.67 when $k = 1$.

We now prove equations 4.66 and 4.67 by induction, so that we assume that $\mathbf{d}_1, \mathbf{d}_2, \ldots, \mathbf{d}_k$ are derived from these results and are mutually conjugate.

The point

$$\mathbf{x}_{k+1} = \mathbf{x}_k + \lambda_k \mathbf{d}_k$$

minimises $f(\mathbf{x}_k + \lambda\mathbf{d}_k)$ along the line $\mathbf{x}_k + \lambda\mathbf{d}_k$.

Thus

$$\mathbf{g}_{k+1}^{\mathrm{T}} \mathbf{d}_k = 0. \tag{4.69}$$

We have

$$\mathbf{x}_{k+1} = \mathbf{x}_k + \lambda_k \mathbf{d}_k$$

$$= \mathbf{x}_{k-1} + \lambda_{k-1} \mathbf{d}_{k-1} + \lambda_k \mathbf{d}_k \text{ etc.}$$

$$\therefore \quad \mathbf{x}_{k+1} = \mathbf{x}_{j+1} + \sum_{i=j+1}^{k} \lambda_i \mathbf{d}_i; \quad 1 \leqslant j \leqslant k-1. \tag{4.70}$$

$$\therefore \quad \mathbf{G}\mathbf{x}_{k+1} = \mathbf{G}\mathbf{x}_{j+1} + \sum_{1=j+1}^{k} \lambda_i \mathbf{G}\mathbf{d}_i$$

$$\therefore \quad \mathbf{g}_{k+1}^{\mathrm{T}} = \mathbf{g}_{j+1}^{\mathrm{T}} + \sum_{i=j+1}^{k} \lambda_i \mathbf{d}_i^{\mathrm{T}} \mathbf{G}, \quad 1 \leqslant j \leqslant k-1.$$

$$\therefore \quad \mathbf{g}_{k+1}^{\mathrm{T}} \mathbf{d}_j = \mathbf{g}_{j+1}^{\mathrm{T}} \mathbf{d}_j + \sum_{i=j+1}^{k} \lambda_i \mathbf{d}_i^{\mathrm{T}} \mathbf{G}\mathbf{d}_j$$

Now $\mathbf{g}_{j+1}^{\mathrm{T}} \mathbf{d}_j = 0$ (in the manner of equations 4.68 and 4.69) and because of the mutual conjugacy $\mathbf{d}_i^{\mathrm{T}} \mathbf{G}\mathbf{d}_j = 0$ for $j < i$. Thus each term on the right is zero.

$$\therefore \quad \mathbf{g}_{k+1}^{\mathrm{T}} \mathbf{d}_j = 0, \quad j = 1, 2, \ldots, k-1, \tag{4.71}$$

and from equation 4.69 we finally have,

$$\mathbf{g}_{k+1}^{\mathrm{T}} \mathbf{d}_j = 0, \quad j = 1, 2, \ldots, k. \tag{4.72}$$

Thus we have shown that $\mathbf{g}_{k+1}$ is orthogonal to each of the directions $\mathbf{d}_1, \mathbf{d}_2, \ldots, \mathbf{d}_k$. We can also show that $\mathbf{g}_{k+1}$ is orthogonal to each of $\mathbf{g}_1, \mathbf{g}_2, \ldots, \mathbf{g}_k$.
From equation 4.72

$$\mathbf{g}_{k+1}^{\mathrm{T}} \mathbf{d}_j = 0, \quad j = 1, 2, \ldots, k$$

and since by the induction hypothesis

$$\mathbf{d}_j = -\mathbf{g}_j + \alpha_{j-1} \mathbf{d}_{j-1},$$

this becomes

$$-\mathbf{g}_{k+1}^{\mathrm{T}} \mathbf{g}_j + \alpha_{j-1} \mathbf{g}_{k+1}^{\mathrm{T}} \mathbf{d}_{j-1} = 0.$$

$$\therefore \quad -\mathbf{g}_{k+1}^{\mathrm{T}} \mathbf{g}_j = 0$$

because $\mathbf{g}_{k+1}^{\mathrm{T}} \mathbf{d}_{j-1} = 0$ from equation 4.72.
Thus

$$\mathbf{g}_{k+1}^{\mathrm{T}} \mathbf{g}_j = 0 \quad \text{for } j = 1, 2, \ldots, k. \tag{4.73}$$

The induction proof is completed by showing that $\mathbf{d}_{k+1}$ defined by equation 4.66 is conjugate to $\mathbf{d}_1, \mathbf{d}_2, \ldots, \mathbf{d}_k$.

For $j = 1, 2, \ldots, k-1$

$$\mathbf{d}_{k+1}^{\mathrm{T}}\,\mathbf{G}\mathbf{d}_j = -\mathbf{g}_{k+1}^{\mathrm{T}}\,\mathbf{G}\mathbf{d}_j + \alpha_k\,\mathbf{d}_k^{\mathrm{T}}\,\mathbf{G}\mathbf{d}_j$$

$$= -\mathbf{g}_{k+1}^{\mathrm{T}}\,\mathbf{G}\mathbf{d}_j$$

because of the mutual conjugacy.

Now

$$-\mathbf{g}_{k+1}^{\mathrm{T}}\,\mathbf{G}\mathbf{d}_j = -\mathbf{g}_{k+1}^{\mathrm{T}}\,\mathbf{G}\,\frac{(\mathbf{x}_{j+1} - \mathbf{x}_j)}{\lambda_j}$$

$$= -\mathbf{g}_{k+1}^{\mathrm{T}}\,\frac{(\mathbf{g}_{j+1} - \mathbf{g}_j)}{\lambda_j}$$

$$= 0$$

on account of equation 4.73.

Thus $\mathbf{d}_{k+1}^{\mathrm{T}}\,\mathbf{G}\mathbf{d}_j = 0$ for $j = 1, 2, \ldots, k-1$ and this will be true whatever the value of α_k. To complete the proof we must determine α_k so that

$$\mathbf{d}_{k+1}^{\mathrm{T}}\,\mathbf{G}\mathbf{d}_k = 0.$$

$$\mathbf{d}_{k+1}^{\mathrm{T}}\,\mathbf{G}\mathbf{d}_k = -\mathbf{g}_{k+1}^{\mathrm{T}}\,\mathbf{G}\mathbf{d}_k + \alpha_k\,\mathbf{d}_k^{\mathrm{T}}\,\mathbf{G}\mathbf{d}_k$$

$$= -\mathbf{g}_{k+1}^{\mathrm{T}}\,\frac{(\mathbf{g}_{k+1} - \mathbf{g}_k)}{\lambda_k} + \alpha_k(-\mathbf{g}_k^{\mathrm{T}} + \alpha_{k-1}\,\mathbf{d}_{k-1}^{\mathrm{T}})\,\frac{(\mathbf{g}_{k+1} - \mathbf{g}_k)}{\lambda_k}.$$

Thus

$$\mathbf{d}_{k+1}^{\mathrm{T}}\,\mathbf{G}\mathbf{d}_k = \frac{-\mathbf{g}_{k+1}^2 + \alpha_k\,\mathbf{g}_k^2}{\lambda_k};$$

all other terms on the right vanish on account of equations 4.72 and 4.73.

Thus $\mathbf{d}_{k+1}$ will be conjugate to $\mathbf{d}_k$ if

$$\alpha_k = \mathbf{g}_{k+1}^2/\mathbf{g}_k^2 \quad \text{as required.}$$

Thus the successive search directions in the Fletcher–Reeves method are conjugate and the method will find the minimum of a quadratic function of n variables after at most n searches. This assumes that the linear searches are carried out exactly and neglects any rounding errors that may arise.

The method will of course be applied to non-quadratic functions. As it homes in on the minimum it will hope to achieve the quadratic convergence property when the quadratic approximation becomes valid. Fletcher and Reeves suggest that in this situation every nth search direction should be along the direction of steepest descent and that the construction of conjugate directions should then *restart*.

The flow chart and the program given include this idea. In general the method does not appear to be so efficient or robust as the Davidon–Fletcher–Powell procedure. Nonetheless it is a useful method.

Flow Chart for Fletcher–Reeves Method

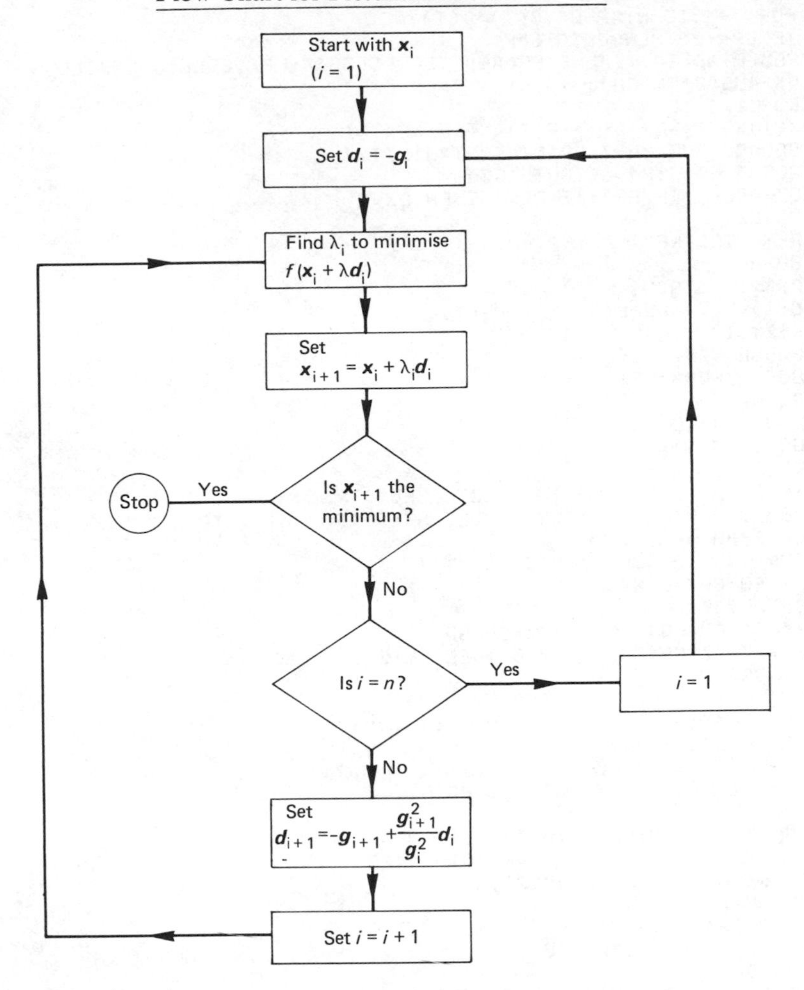


```
READY.

 100 PRINT"MINIMISATION BY FLETCHER-REEVES"
 120 REM LINEAR SEARCHES BY CUBIC INTERPOLATION
 150 REM F(X1,X2..XN) AT 5000;G(1),G(2)...G(N) AT 6000
 200 PRINT"NUMBER OF VARIABLES":INPUT N
 220 DIM X,Y,P,Q,D,G(N)
 300 PRINT"INITIAL VALUES"
 320 FOR I=1 TO N:PRINT"X"I,:INPUT X(I):NEXT I:PRINT""
 340 REM SET SEARCH COUNT
 350 SV=1
 360 REM INTERMEDIATE OUTPUT
 380 PRINT"           CURRENT VALUES"
 550 FOR I=1 TO N:P(I)=X(I):PRINT"X"I"="X(I):NEXT I
 560 GOSUB 5000:FP=Z:PRINT"Z="Z
 570 GOSUB 6000:G1=G0:GK=G0
 575 REM SET FIRST SEARCH IN STEEPEST DESCENT DIRECTION
 580 FOR I=1 TO N:D(I)=-G(I):NEXT I
 585 REM K COUNTS THE SEARCHES
 590 K=1
```

```
600 GP=0
610 FOR I=1 TO N:GP=GP+G(I)*D(I):NEXT I
620 IF GP<=0 THEN GOTO 680
625 REM FIND INITIAL STEP AND IF NECESSARY REVERSE DOWNHILL
630 QX=ABS(2*FP/GP): IF QX>1 THEN QX=1
640 FOR I=1 TO N
650 X(I)=P(I)-QX*D(I):P(I)=X(I):NEXT I
660 GOSUB 5000:FP=Z:PRINT"INSTABILITY"
670 GOSUB 6000:G1=G0:GOTO 600
680 QX=ABS(2*FP/GP):IF QX>1 THEN QX=1
690 HH=QX
700 REM FIND NEXT POINT
710 BB=HH
720 FOR I=1 TO N
730 Q(I)=P(I)+BB*D(I):X(I)=Q(I)
740 NEXT I
750 GOSUB 5000:FQ=Z
760 GOSUB 6000:G2=G0
770 GQ=0
780 FOR I=1 TO N
790 GQ=GQ+G(I)*D(I)
800 NEXT I
810 IF GQ>0  OR FQ>FP THEN GOTO 860
815 REM DO INTERPOLATION DOUBLE STEP AND SHIFT TO Q
820 HH=2*HH
830 FOR I=1 TO N:P(I)=Q(I):NEXT I
840 FP=FQ:GP=GQ:G1=G2
850 GOTO 710
860 ZZ=3*(FP-FQ)/HH:ZZ=ZZ+GP+GQ
870 WW=ZZ*ZZ-GP*GQ:IF WW<0 THEN WW=0
880 W=SQR(WW)
890 DD=HH*(1-(GQ+W-ZZ)/(GQ-GP+2*W))
900 FOR I=1 TO N:X(I)=P(I)+DD*D(I):NEXT I
910 GOSUB 5000:FR=Z
920 GOSUB 6000:G3=G0
925 REM FIND GRADIENT AT NEW POINT
930 GR=0
940 FOR I=1 TO N:GR=GR+G(I)*D(I):NEXT I
950 IF Z<=FP AND Z<=FQ THEN GOTO 1100
960 IF GR>0 THEN GOTO 1020
990 HH=HH-DD
1000 FOR I=1 TO N:P(I)=X(I):NEXT I
1010 FP=Z:GP=GR:GOTO 860
1020 HH=DD
1030 FOR I=1 TO N:Q(I)=X(I):NEXT I
1040 FQ=Z:GQ=GR:GOTO 860
1100 REM TERMINATION TEST
1110 IF G3<0.000001 THEN GOTO 1300
1120 IF K=N THEN GOTO 1250
1130 REM COUNT SEARCHES
1140 K=K+1
1150 REM FIND CONJUGATE DIRECTION
1160 AK=G3*G3/(GK*GK)
1170 FOR I=1 TO N:D(I)=-G(I)+AK*D(I):P(I)=X(I):NEXT I
1200 PRINT "NEW DIRECTION";:DV=DV+1:PRINT"       SEARCH"DV
1210 FP=Z:G1=G0:GK=G0
1220 FOR I=1 TO N:PRINT"X"I"="X(I):NEXT I:PRINT "Z="Z
1230 GOTO 600
1250 PRINT"RESTART";:SV=SV+1:DV=DV+1
1260 PRINT"            ITERATION"SV;"SEARCH";DV
1270 PRINT""
1280 GOTO 550
1300 PRINT"MINIMUM FOUND"
1320 FOR I=1 TO N:PRINT"X"I"="X(I):NEXT I
1340 PRINT"FUNCTION MINIMUM="Z
```

```
 135Ø PRINT"FUNCTION EVALUATIONS=";TV
 14ØØ END
 5ØØØ Z=1ØØ*(X(2)-X(1)*X(1))↑2
 5Ø1Ø Z=Z+(1-X(1))↑2
 5Ø2Ø TV=TV+1
 51ØØ RETURN
 6ØØØ GØ=Ø
 61ØØ G(1)=-4ØØ*X(1)*(X(2)-X(1)*X(1))
 611Ø G(1)=G(1)-2*(1-X(1))
 62ØØ G(2)=2ØØ*(X(2)-X(1)*X(1))
 7ØØØ FOR I=1 TO N:GØ=GØ+G(I)*G(I):NEXT I
 71ØØ GØ=SQR(GØ)
 75ØØ RETURN
READY.
```

Example 1

Use the Fletcher–Reeves method with starting point (−1·2, 1) to minimise Rosenbrock's function

$$f(x_1, x_2) = 100(x_2 - x_1^2)^2 + (1 - x_1)^2.$$

This is a particularly awkward starting point for this function. The function itself is also a very tricky one to minimise. The minimum is zero at (1, 1). The start and finish of the output is shown.

```
MINIMISATION BY FLETCHER-REEVES
NUMBER OF VARIABLES   2
INITIAL VALUES
X 1  -1.2       X 2   1
          CURRENT VALUES
X 1 =-1.2
X 2 = 1
Z= 24.2
NEW DIRECTION          SEARCH 1
X 1 =-1.Ø3Ø19958
X 2 = 1.Ø693Ø629
Z= 4.1281Ø253
RESTART          ITERATION 2 SEARCH 2

X 1 =-.734332831
X 2 = .463358712
Z= 3.5837788
NEW DIRECTION          SEARCH 3
X 1 =-.69221993
X 2 = .488171727
Z= 2.87171423
RESTART          ITERATION 3 SEARCH 4

X 1 =-.596847682
X 2 = .324267541
Z= 2.652Ø6421
NEW DIRECTION          SEARCH 5
X 1 =-.572697979
X 2 = .338529113
Z= 2.4845Ø1Ø4

..........................................

RESTART          ITERATION 2Ø SEARCH 38

X 1 = .999998519
X 2 = .999996691
Z= 1.42287792E-11
```

```
NEW DIRECTION          SEARCH 39
X 1 = .999998383
X 2 = .99999676
Z= 2.61777331E-12
RESTART            ITERATION 21 SEARCH 40

X 1 = .999998436
X 2 = .999996897
Z= 2.51216973E-12
NEW DIRECTION          SEARCH 41
X 1 = .999998449
X 2 = .999996892
Z= 2.40877434E-12
RESTART            ITERATION 22 SEARCH 42

X 1 = .999999914
X 2 = .999999861
Z= 1.12120654E-13
MINIMUM FOUND
X 1 = .999999927
X 2 = .999999854
FUNCTION MINIMUM= 5.31633113E-15
FUNCTION EVALUATIONS= 123
```

Example 2

Find the minimum of

$$f(x_1, x_2, x_3) = 3(x_1 - 1)^2 + 2(x_2 - 2)^2 + (x_3 - 3)^2.$$

In contrast to Example 1 this is a trivial problem. The starting point used was (9, −7, 11). The output given illustrates that, in accordance with theory, the Fletcher–Reeves method locates the minimum after three searches.

```
MINIMISATION BY FLETCHER-REEVES
NUMBER OF VARIABLES    3
INITIAL VALUES
X 1     9        X 2     -7        X 3    11
          CURRENT VALUES

X 1 = 9
X 2 =-7
X 3 = 11
Z= 418
NEW DIRECTION          SEARCH 1
X 1 =-.481967211
X 2 = .111475408
X 3 = 7.83934426
Z= 37.1709836
NEW DIRECTION          SEARCH 2
X 1 = 1.20689655
X 2 = 2.82758621
X 3 = 4.86206897
Z= 4.96551725
MINIMUM FOUND
X 1 = 1
X 2 = 2
X 3 = 3
FUNCTION MINIMUM= 1.73472348E-18
FUNCTION EVALUATIONS= 8
```

4.5 References

The last twenty-five years have witnessed a great deal of research activity in the area discussed in this chapter. Many papers have been published and many advances have been made. The methods discussed in this chapter are but three among many that have been suggested. The ideas of conjugate directions and the property of quadratic functions as suggested by equation 4.17 are fundamental. It was mentioned in Section 4.3 that the updating of the **H** matrix in the D.F.P. method was not the only one possible. Indeed Huang has shown that there is a whole family of methods based on these ideas, of which the Davidon–Fletcher–Powell and the Fletcher–Reeves are but two special cases. The references below are just a selection from many which could have been quoted.

1 C. G. Broyden, 'Quasi-Newton methods and their application to function minimisation', *Maths. of Comp.*, **21**, 368–381, 1967.
2 C. G. Broyden, 'The convergence of single-rank quasi-Newton methods', *Maths. of Comp.*, **24**, 376–382, 1970.
3 R. Fletcher, 'A new approach to variable metric algorithms', *The Comp. Journal*, **13**, 317–322, 1970.
4 R. Fletcher and M. J. D. Powell, 'A rapidly convergent descent method for minimisation', *The Comp. Journal*, **6**, 163–168, 1963.
5 R. Fletcher and C. M. Reeves, 'Function minimisation by conjugate gradients', *The Comp. Journal*, **7**, 149–154, 1964.
6 H. Y. Huang, 'Unified approach to quadratically convergent algorithms for function minimisation', *J. Opt. Theory App.*, **5**, 405–423, 1970.
7 H. Y. Huang and A. V. Levy, 'Numerical experiments on quadratically convergent algorithms for function minimisation', *J. Opt. Theory App.*, **6**, 269–282, 1970.
8 M. J. D. Powell, 'On the convergence of the variable metric algorithm', *J. Inst. Maths. App.*, **7**, 21–36, 1971.
9 M. J. D. Powell, 'Quadratic termination properties of minimisation algorithms. I. Statement and discussion of results', *J.Inst. Maths. App.*, **10**, 333–342, 1972.
10 M. J. D. Powell, 'Quadratic termination properties of minimisation algorithms. II. Proofs of theorems', *J. Inst. Maths. App.*, **10**, 343–357, 1972.

Exercises 4

1 Modify the steepest descent program given in Section 4.1 to carry out the linear searches (i) by Fibonacci search (ii) by Golden search (iii) by cubic interpolation. Try to use your program to solve the problems of the worked examples. Note any difficulties that arise.

2 Attempt to solve Examples 1 and 2 of Section 4.1 with different starting points. Do any difficulties arise?

3 If P_0, P_1, and P_2 are successive points obtained from using the method of steepest descent it has been suggested that the method can be accelerated by making the next search in the direction P_0P_2. Draw a sketch of the contours of a function near its minimum to illustrate the thinking behind this suggestion. Try to incorporate this idea into the program given in Section 4.1.

4 If $f(\mathbf{x})$ is a positive definite quadratic function of two variables, whose minimum is at the origin, and $\mathbf{x}_0$, $\mathbf{x}_1$, and $\mathbf{x}_2$ are three successive points in a sequence using the method of steepest descent, show that the line through $\mathbf{x}_0$ and $\mathbf{x}_2$ passes through the minimum point of the function. See the acceleration technique of the previous question.

5 Consider the quadratic function $f(x, y) = x^2/a^2 + y^2/b^2$ where a and b are constants. The contours of this function are the ellipses

$$\frac{x^2}{a^2} + \frac{y^2}{b^2} = c^2,$$

where c^2 is the function value. The function minimum is of course zero at the origin. Show that the line

$$y = mx \pm c\sqrt{(a^2 m^2 + b^2)}$$

is tangential to this ellipse and touches it at the point P,

$$\left[\pm \frac{ma^2 c}{\sqrt{(a^2 m^2 + b^2)}}, \pm \frac{cb^2}{\sqrt{(a^2 m^2 + b^2)}}\right].$$

Thus a search from a point on this line along the line will find the function minimum at P. The gradient of the line joining P to the origin (the minimum point) is m'. Show that

$$mm' = -b^2/a^2.$$

Show that this is equivalent to

$$\mathbf{p}^{\mathrm{T}} \begin{pmatrix} 1/a^2 & 0 \\ 0 & 1/b^2 \end{pmatrix} \mathbf{q} = 0$$

where $\mathbf{p}^{\mathrm{T}} = (\cos \alpha, \sin \alpha)$, $\mathbf{q}^{\mathrm{T}} = (\cos \beta, \sin \beta)$ and $m = \tan \alpha$, $m' = \tan \beta$. Thus $\mathbf{p}$ and $\mathbf{q}$ are conjugate, and a search along $\mathbf{p}$, followed by a search in the direction $\mathbf{q}$ will find the minimum after two searches.

6 Minimise

$$f(\mathbf{x}) = 3(x_1 - 4)^2 + 5(x_2 + 3)^2 + 7(2x_3 + 1)^2$$

using (a) the D.F.P. method (b) the Fletcher–Reeves method. Show that as expected (a) needs 3 iterations and (b) needs 3 searches whatever starting point is used.

7 Minimise

$$f(x_1, x_2) = 1 - 2x_1 - 2x_2 - 4x_1 x_2 + 10x_1^2 + 2x_2^2.$$

8 Minimise

$$x_1^4 + x_2^4 + 2x_1^2 x_2^2 - 4x_1 + 3.$$

9 Minimise

$$(x_1^2 + x_2 - 11)^2 + (x_1 + x_2^2 - 7)^2.$$

10 Minimise

$$f(x_1, x_2) = x_1^3 + x_2^2 - 3x_1 - 2x_2 + 2.$$

Part II
Constrained Optimisation

5

General Theory

5.1 Equality Constraints

Consider the two variable problem to minimise

$$z = f(x, y)$$

where the two variables x and y are constrained by the relationship

$$g(x, y) = 0. \tag{5.1}$$

In principle we can use the constraint $g(x, y) = 0$ to solve for y as a function of x, viz. $y = h(x)$. In practice of course, it might be difficult or even impossible to find an explicit form for $h(x)$. However, subject to certain differentiability conditions (which must be satisfied for our results to hold) we shall have for the derivative of $h(x)$

$$\frac{\mathrm{d}y}{\mathrm{d}x} = \frac{\mathrm{d}}{\mathrm{d}x}\, h(x) = -\frac{\partial g}{\partial x}\Big/\frac{\partial g}{\partial y}\,. \tag{5.2}$$

We can then regard

$$z = f(x, y) = f[x, h(x)] \tag{5.3}$$

as a function of the one independent variable x. For a minimum of z the necessary condition is

$$\frac{\mathrm{d}z}{\mathrm{d}x} = \frac{\partial f}{\partial x} + \frac{\partial f}{\partial y}\frac{\mathrm{d}y}{\mathrm{d}x} = 0$$

$$\text{i.e.} \quad \frac{\partial f}{\partial x} + \left(\frac{-\dfrac{\partial f}{\partial y}}{\dfrac{\partial g}{\partial y}}\right) \cdot \frac{\partial g}{\partial x} = 0. \tag{5.4}$$

5.1 and 5.4 are equations which in principle can be solved to yield values x^*, y^* at the minimum.

We can put this result in a slightly different form. If we define

$$\lambda = \frac{-\partial f}{\partial y}(x, y)\Big/\frac{\partial g}{\partial y}(x, y) \tag{5.5}$$

when $x = x^*$, $y = y^*$, then at the minimum we shall have

$$g(x, y) = 0,$$

$$\frac{\partial f}{\partial x}(x, y) + \lambda \frac{\partial g}{\partial x}(x, y) = 0,$$

and

$$\frac{\partial f}{\partial y}(x, y) + \lambda \frac{\partial g}{\partial y}(x, y) = 0,$$

the last result following directly from equation 5.5.

A neat way of generating these three necessary conditions is to consider the *Lagrange function*

$$F(x, y, \lambda) = f(x, y) + \lambda g(x, y) \tag{5.6}$$

which is the sum of the objective function and the product of λ (the Lagrange multiplier) with the constraint. The necessary conditions for a constrained minimum of $f(x, y)$ can then be written as:

$$\left.\begin{aligned} \frac{\partial F}{\partial x}(x, y, \lambda) &= \frac{\partial f}{\partial x}(x, y) + \lambda \frac{\partial g}{\partial x}(x, y) = 0 \\ \frac{\partial F}{\partial y}(x, y, \lambda) &= \frac{\partial f}{\partial y}(x, y) + \lambda \frac{\partial g}{\partial y}(x, y) = 0 \\ \frac{\partial F}{\partial \lambda}(x, y, \lambda) &= g(x, y) = 0 \end{aligned}\right\} \tag{5.7}$$

These provide three equations for x^*, y^* and λ^*, the values of x, y, and λ at the minimum.

Example 1

Find the minimum of $x^2 + y^2$ subject to $x + y = 4$. Here $f(x, y) = x^2 + y^2$ and $g(x, y) = 4 - x - y = 0$.

The Lagrange function is

$$F(x, y, \lambda) = x^2 + y^2 + \lambda(4 - x - y),$$

$$\frac{\partial F}{\partial x} = 2x - \lambda = 0$$

$$\frac{\partial F}{\partial y} = 2y - \lambda = 0$$

$$\frac{\partial F}{\partial \lambda} = 4 - x - y = 0.$$

The solution to these equations is easily seen to be $x = y = 2$, $\lambda = 4$.

The function minimum is $2^2 + 2^2 = 8$. It is left as an exercise for the reader to verify this result by considering the function of one variable x obtained by eliminating y,

$$z = x^2 + (4 - x)^2.$$

The result (equation 5.7) can be generalised to functions of n variables which are subject to m equation constraints although we argue the case somewhat differently.

Thus we consider the problem of minimising

$$z = f(\mathbf{x}) = f(x_1, x_2, \ldots, x_n)$$

where the variables $\mathbf{x}$ are constrained by

$$g_1(\mathbf{x}) = 0, g_2(\mathbf{x}) = 0, \ldots, g_m(\mathbf{x}) = 0. \tag{5.8}$$

In principle we can use the constraints to express m of the variables (which we can without loss of generality take to be $x_1, x_2, \ldots, x_m$) in terms of the other $n - m$. We can think of these as being the $n - m$ independent variables. Provided this can be done in principle we can say that at the constrained minimum

$$f(\mathbf{x} + \mathbf{h}) - f(\mathbf{x}) \geqslant 0 \quad \text{for all } \mathbf{h} \text{ which satisfy } g_i(\mathbf{x} + \mathbf{h}) = g_i(\mathbf{x}) = 0; \quad i = 1, \ldots, m$$

Thus to first order in h_j we shall have

$$\sum_{j=1}^{n} h_j \frac{\partial f}{\partial x_j} = 0 \quad \text{where the } h_j \text{ must satisfy}$$

$$\sum_{j=1}^{n} h_j \frac{\partial g_i}{\partial x_j} = 0, \quad \text{for } i = 1, 2, \ldots, m.$$

This we can write as

$$\sum_{j=1}^{n} h_j \left(\frac{\partial f}{\partial x_j} + \sum_{i=1}^{m} \lambda_i \frac{\partial g_i}{\partial x_j} \right) = 0, \tag{5.9}$$

where $\lambda_1, \lambda_2, \ldots, \lambda_m$ are the m Lagrange multipliers.

Since $h_{m+1}, h_{m+2}, \ldots, h_n$ are independent increments their coefficients must be zero;

$$\text{i.e.} \quad \frac{\partial f}{\partial x_j} + \sum_{i=1}^{m} \lambda_i \frac{\partial g_i}{\partial x_j} = 0, \quad j = m + 1, \ldots, n.$$

The increments $h_1, h_2, \ldots, h_m$ are not independent but we can make their coefficients in equation 5.9 zero by choice of $\lambda_1, \lambda_2, \ldots, \lambda_m$.

Thus we choose $\lambda_1, \lambda_2, \ldots, \lambda_m$ to make

$$\frac{\partial f}{\partial x_j} + \sum_{i=1}^{m} \lambda_i \frac{\partial g_i}{\partial x_j} = 0 \quad \text{for } j = 1, 2, \ldots, m.$$

Thus we have finally

$$\frac{\partial f}{\partial x_j} + \sum_{i=1}^{m} \lambda_i \frac{\partial g_i}{\partial x_j} = 0, \quad j = 1, 2, \ldots, n. \tag{5.10}$$

Thus if we define the Lagrange function

$$F(\mathbf{x}, \boldsymbol{\lambda}) = f(\mathbf{x}) + \sum_{i=1}^{m} \lambda_i g_i(\mathbf{x}) \tag{5.11}$$

then the necessary conditions for the constrained minimum of $f(\mathbf{x})$ can be expressed as

$$\frac{\partial F}{\partial x_j} = \frac{\partial f}{\partial x_j} + \sum_{i=1}^{m} \lambda_i \frac{\partial g_i}{\partial x_j} = 0, \quad j = 1, 2, \ldots, n \tag{5.12}$$

$$\frac{\partial F}{\partial \lambda_i} = g_i(\mathbf{x}) = 0; \quad i = 1, \ldots, m. \tag{5.13}$$

We note that for feasible values of $\mathbf{x}$ (i.e. those which satisfy the constraints)

$$F(\mathbf{x}, \boldsymbol{\lambda}) = f(\mathbf{x}) + \sum_{i=1}^{m} \lambda_i g_i(\mathbf{x}) = f(\mathbf{x}).$$

At the constrained minimum $\mathbf{x}^*$

$$f(\mathbf{x}^* + \mathbf{h}) - f(\mathbf{x}^*) \geqslant 0 \quad \text{where } \mathbf{h} \text{ satisfies } g_i(\mathbf{x}^* + \mathbf{h}) = 0 \text{ for all } i.$$

We shall thus have

$$F(\mathbf{x}^* + \mathbf{h}) - F(\mathbf{x}^*) = \sum_{j=1}^{n} \frac{\partial F}{\partial x_j} h_j + \tfrac{1}{2} \sum_{i=1}^{n} \sum_{j=1}^{n} h_i \frac{\partial^2 F}{\partial x_i \, \partial x_j} h_j + \cdots \geqslant 0,$$

where the derivatives are evaluated at $\mathbf{x}^*$, λ^*.

On account of equation 5.12 this gives

$$\tfrac{1}{2} \sum_{i=1}^{n} \sum_{j=1}^{n} h_i \frac{\partial^2 F}{\partial x_i \, \partial x_j} h_j \geqslant 0, \quad \text{for all } \mathbf{h} \text{ which satisfy the constraints.}$$

Sufficient conditions for a constrained minimum are thus equation 5.12, and equation 5.13 and the quadratic form

$$\tfrac{1}{2} \sum_{i=1}^{n} \sum_{j=1}^{n} h_i \frac{\partial^2 F}{\partial x_i \, \partial x_j} h_j \tag{5.14}$$

is positive definite for values for $\mathbf{h}$ satisfying the constraints.

N.B. It is not always easy to put this last condition in a useful form.

Example 2

Verify that (2,2) is the constrained minimum of $x_1^2 + x_2^2$ subject to $x_1 + x_2 = 4$.

With $F(\mathbf{x}, \lambda) = x_1^2 + x_2^2 + \lambda(4 - x_1 - x_2)$ we have seen that

$$\frac{\partial F}{\partial x_1} = 0, \quad \frac{\partial F}{\partial x_2} = 0, \quad \frac{\partial F}{\partial \lambda} = 0 \quad \text{when } x_1 = x_2 = 2 \text{ and } \lambda = 4.$$

The Hessian matrix for F is $\begin{pmatrix} 2 & 0 \\ 0 & 2 \end{pmatrix}$ and this is simply positive definite, which establishes the result.

5.2 Inequality Constraints

In this section we extend the ideas of Lagrange multipliers to the case of inequality constraints. Thus we consider the general mathematical programming problem:

minimise $\quad f(\mathbf{x})$

subject to the m constraints $\quad g_i(\mathbf{x}) \leqslant b_i \quad (i = 1, 2, \ldots, m).$

There is of course no loss of generality in assuming that all constraints are of the less than or equal to variety. (The constraint $\phi(\mathbf{x}) \geqslant c$ can be written as $-\phi(\mathbf{x}) \leqslant -c$.)

Perhaps at the outset we should say that there is no solution to the problem posed in all cases. To date no method has been devised which is guaranteed to solve every problem of the type just given. Perhaps the reader will remedy this situation.

The inequality constraints can be transformed into equation constraints by the addition of a non-negative *slack variable* u_i^2 to each one (note u_i^2 is always positive) to obtain

$$g_i(\mathbf{x}) + u_i^2 = b_i$$

$$\text{i.e.} \quad g_i(\mathbf{x}) + u_i^2 - b_i = 0. \tag{5.15}$$

Thus the problem is to minimise $f(\mathbf{x})$ subject to the m equation constraints $g_i(\mathbf{x}) + u_i^2 - b_i = 0$. In line with the previous section we form the Lagrange function

$$F(\mathbf{x}, \boldsymbol{\lambda}, \mathbf{u}) = f(\mathbf{x}) + \sum_{i=1}^{m} \lambda_i[g_i(\mathbf{x}) + u_i^2 - b_i]. \tag{5.16}$$

The necessary conditions to be satisfied at a stationary point are:

$$\frac{\partial F}{\partial x_j} = 0 = \frac{\partial f}{\partial x_j} + \sum_{i=1}^{m} \lambda_i \frac{\partial g_i}{\partial x_j}; \quad j = 1, 2, \ldots, n \tag{5.17}$$

$$\frac{\partial F}{\partial \lambda_i} = 0 = g_i(\mathbf{x}) + u_i^2 - b_i; \quad i = 1, 2, \ldots, m \tag{5.18}$$

$$\frac{\partial F}{\partial u_i} = 0 = 2\lambda_i u_i. \quad i = 1, 2, \ldots, m. \tag{5.19}$$

The last condition when multiplied by $u_i/2$ gives

$$\lambda_i u_i^2 = 0$$

$$\text{i.e.} \quad \lambda_i[b_i - g_i(\mathbf{x})] = 0, \quad i = 1, 2, \ldots, m. \tag{5.20}$$

Equations 5.17, 5.18 and 5.20 are necessary conditions for a constrained minimum $\mathbf{x}^*$. Equations 5.18 are just a restatement of the constraints $g_i(\mathbf{x}) \leqslant 0$. Condition 5.20 states that one of λ_i or $b_i - g_i(\mathbf{x}^*)$ is zero. If λ_i is not zero then $g_i(\mathbf{x}^*) = b_i$, and the constraint is *active* and satisfied as an equation. On the other hand if the constraint is satisfied as a strict inequality so that $g_i(\mathbf{x}^*) < b$ then the corresponding Lagrange multiplier λ_i is zero. This makes sense intuitively. As far as the constrained minimum is concerned if $g_i(\mathbf{x}^*) < b_i$, this constraint is inactive and could be ignored, and the corresponding λ_i is zero. Of course at the outset we do not know which constraints can be ignored.

There is also an extra condition which must be satisfied at a constrained minimum, viz. $\lambda_i \geqslant 0$.

Suppose that equations 5.17, 5.18 and 5.20 are satisfied at the point $(\mathbf{x}^*, \boldsymbol{\lambda}^*, \mathbf{u}^*)$. If the actual constrained function minimum is $z = f(\mathbf{x}^*)$ then we can regard z as a function of the b_i, in that changing the b_i will modify the constraints and so will change z. We shall show that

$$\frac{\partial z}{\partial b_i} = -\lambda_i^*.$$

$$\frac{\partial z}{\partial b_i} = \sum_{j=1}^{n} \frac{\partial f}{\partial x_j} \cdot \frac{\partial x_j}{\partial b_i}$$

where the partial derivatives are evaluated at $\mathbf{x}^*$.

Since $g_k(\mathbf{x}) + u_k^2 = b_k$

$$\frac{\partial g_k}{\partial b_i} = \sum_{j=1}^{n} \frac{\partial g_k}{\partial x_j} \cdot \frac{\partial x_j}{\partial b_i} = \begin{matrix} 0 & \text{if } i \neq k \\ 1 & \text{if } i = k. \end{matrix}$$

Thus

$$\frac{\partial z}{\partial b_i} + \sum_{k=1}^{m} \lambda_k^* \frac{\partial g_k}{\partial b_i} = \frac{\partial z}{\partial b_i} + \lambda_i^* = \sum_{j=1}^{n} \left(\frac{\partial f}{\partial x_j} + \sum_{k=1}^{m} \lambda_k^* \frac{\partial g_k}{\partial x_j} \right) \frac{\partial x_j}{\partial b_i}.$$

But this is zero because of equations 5.17.

Thus

$$\frac{\partial z}{\partial b_i} = -\lambda_i^*. \tag{5.21}$$

Now as b_i is increased the constraint region is enlarged which cannot possibly result in a higher value for z, the minimum of $f(\mathbf{x})$ within this region, although it could reduce z. So we shall have

$$\frac{\partial z}{\partial b_i} \leqslant 0$$

$$\text{i.e.} \quad \lambda_i^* \geqslant 0. \tag{5.22}$$

The necessary conditions to be satisfied at the minimum of $f(\mathbf{x})$ where $\mathbf{x}$ must satisfy $g_i(\mathbf{x}) \leqslant b_i$ $(i = 1, 2, \ldots, m)$ are that we can find $\mathbf{x}$ and $\boldsymbol{\lambda}$ which satisfy

$$\left.\begin{aligned} \frac{\partial f}{\partial x_j} + \sum_{i=1}^{m} \lambda_i \frac{\partial g_i}{\partial x_j} &= 0, \quad j = 1, \ldots, n. \\ g_i(\mathbf{x}) &\leqslant b_i \quad i = 1, 2, \ldots, m. \\ \lambda_i[g_i(\mathbf{x}) - b_i] &= 0 \quad i = 1, 2, \ldots, m. \\ \lambda_i &\geqslant 0. \quad i = 1, \ldots, m. \end{aligned}\right\} \tag{5.23}$$

[The sign of the λ_i is reversed if we are dealing with a maximum.] These conditions are known as the Kuhn–Tucker conditions.

Example 1

Write down the Kuhn–Tucker conditions for the minimum of $3x_1^2 + 4x_1x_2 + 5x_2^2$ subject to $x_1 \geqslant 0$, $x_2 \geqslant 0$ and $x_1 + x_2 \geqslant 4$.

The problem can be written, minimise

$$3x_1^2 + 4x_1x_2 + 5x_2^2$$

subject to

$$-x_1 \leqslant 0$$

$$-x_2 \leqslant 0$$

$$-x_1 - x_2 \leqslant -4.$$

The Lagrange function $F(\mathbf{x}, \mathbf{u}, \boldsymbol{\lambda})$ is

$$F = 3x_1^2 + 4x_1x_2 + 5x_2^2 + \lambda_1(u_1^2 - x_1) + \lambda_2(u_2^2 - x_2) + \lambda_3(u_3^2 - x_1 - x_2 + 4).$$

The necessary conditions are thus

$$6x_1 + 4x_2 - \lambda_1 - \lambda_3 = 0$$

$$4x_1 + 10x_2 - \lambda_2 - \lambda_3 = 0$$

$$-x_1 \leqslant 0, \quad -x_2 \leqslant 0, \quad -x_1 - x_2 \leqslant -4,$$

$$\lambda_1 x_1 = 0, \quad \lambda_2 x_2 = 0, \quad \lambda_3(4 - x_1 - x_2) = 0$$

$$\lambda_1, \lambda_2, \lambda_3 \geqslant 0.$$

It is easy to verify that these conditions are satisfied by $x_1 = 3$, $x_2 = 1$, $\lambda_1 = 0$, $\lambda_2 = 0$, $\lambda_3 = 22$, the function minimum being 44 at A(3, 1).

The contours of $f(\mathbf{x})$ are the ellipses

$$3x_1^2 + 4x_1x_2 + 5x_2^2 = c.$$

The unconstrained minimum of $f(\mathbf{x})$ is zero at the origin. The constrained region is shown shaded in Fig. 5.1 which illustrates the problem.

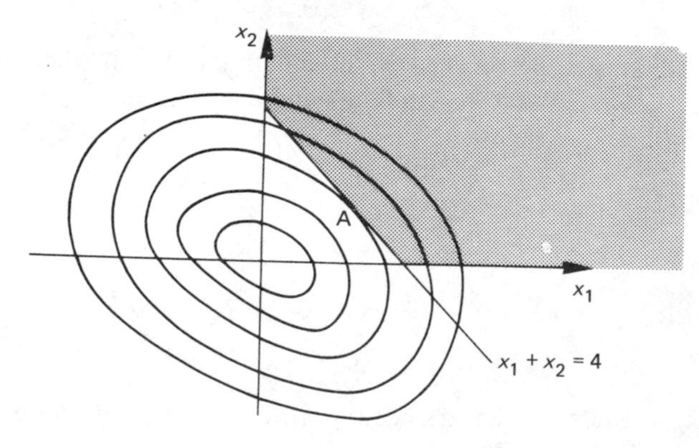

Figure 5.1

5.3 Convexity and Concavity

The general mathematical programming problem posed at the beginning of the previous section is a very hard problem. Indeed it is one to which there is no complete solution as yet. Some of the difficulties can be illustrated graphically for some two variable problems. Figures 5.2(a) and (b) show the contours of a function. The values increase as we move from $\mathbf{x}^*$, the unconstrained minimum. Also shown are the constraint boundaries $g_i(\mathbf{x}) = b_i$, the constrained region being shaded.

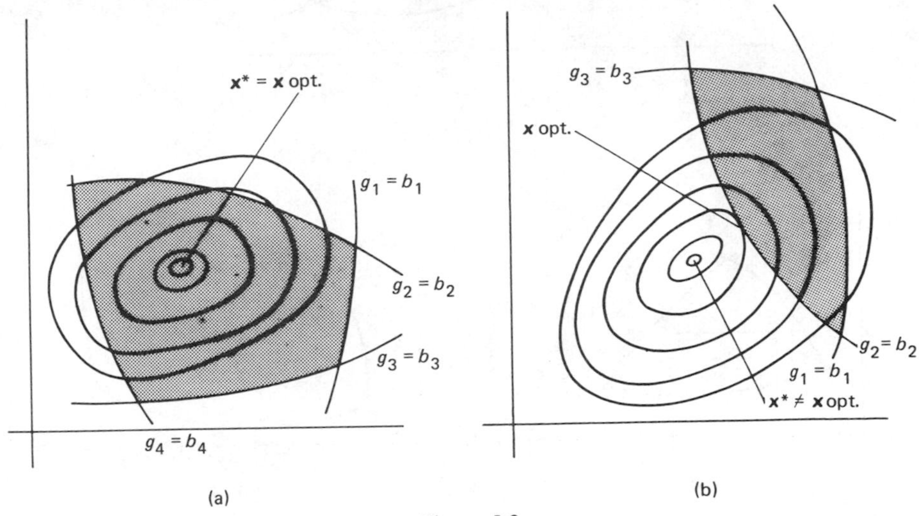

Figure 5.2

In (a) the constrained minimum is the same as the unconstrained minimum. All the constraints are satisfied as strict inequalities and if we *had only known* we could have ignored the constraints and treated this problem by the methods of Part I of this book. In (b) the constrained minimum lies on $g_2(\mathbf{x}) = b_2$ and the other two constraints are inactive. If we *had only known* we could have ignored g_1 and g_3 and treated this as an equation constraint problem just involving $g_2(\mathbf{x}) = b_2$. Incidentally, we notice from this that at the constrained minimum $\mathbf{x}$ opt., $\nabla f(\mathbf{x}) = \lambda \nabla g_2(\mathbf{x})$ since $\nabla f(\mathbf{x})$ is perpendicular to the contour and the boundary at this point. (Compare this with equation 5.17.)

It is also possible for the constraints to introduce local minima into the problem. This can occur even if the function itself only has one minimum point in the unconstrained situation. Figure 5.3 illustrates this.

The function has only one unconstrained minimum point. However, for the constrained problem both A and B are local minima since no feasible point in the immediate neighbourhood of A or B gives smaller function values.

Some of the problems just discussed are eliminated if we restrict our problems to constraint regions that are convex and the function to be minimised (maximised) is convex (concave).

We first define these terms. A region is *convex* if the line segment joining any two points in the region lies entirely within the region. Thus if $\mathbf{x}_1$ and $\mathbf{x}_2$ are in the region so is every point $\theta \mathbf{x}_2 + (1 - \theta)\mathbf{x}_1$ where $0 < \theta < 1$. Figure 5.4(a) illustrates a convex region, Fig. 5.4(b) a non convex region.

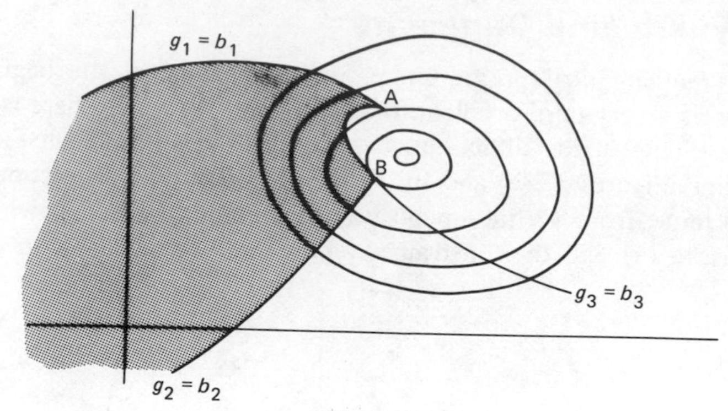

Figure 5.3

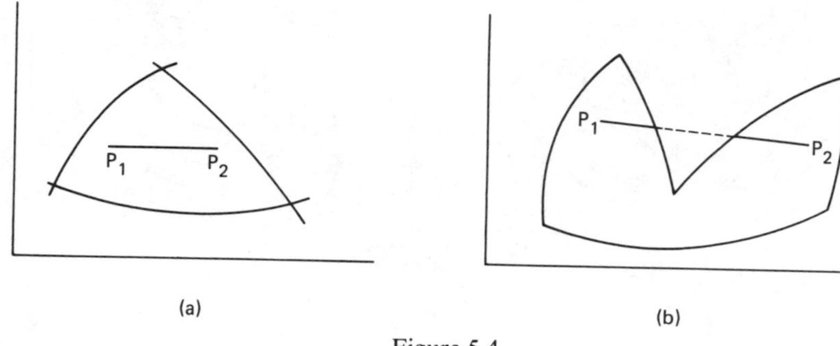

Figure 5.4

A function $f(\mathbf{x})$ is said to be *convex* over the convex domain X if for any two points $\mathbf{x}_1, \mathbf{x}_2 \in X$,

$$f[\theta \mathbf{x}_2 + (1-\theta)\,\mathbf{x}_1] \leqslant \theta f(\mathbf{x}_2) + (1-\theta)\,f(\mathbf{x}_1) \tag{5.24}$$

for $0 < \theta < 1$.

For a function of one variable this means that it lies below the chord joining any two points on its graph (Fig. 5.5).

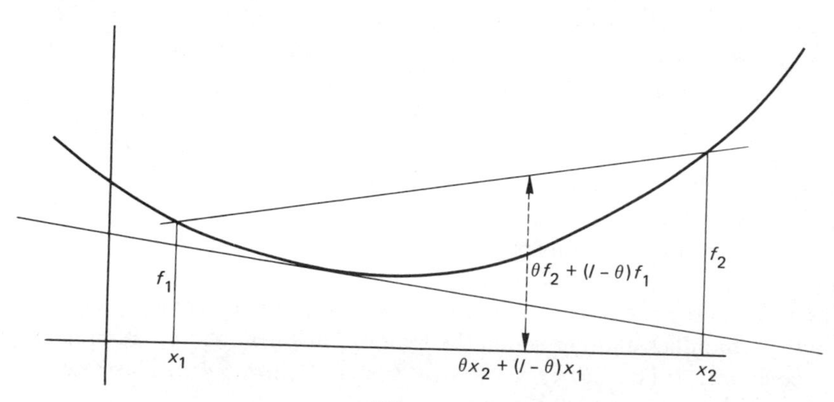

Figure 5.5

For a *concave* function defined on a convex domain we reverse the inequality to obtain,

$$f[\theta \mathbf{x}_2 + (1-\theta)\mathbf{x}_1] \geqslant \theta f(\mathbf{x}_2) + (1-\theta) f(\mathbf{x}_1). \tag{5.25}$$

Such a function lies above the chord joining two points on its graph.

If the inequalities in equations 5.24 and 5.25 are replaced by strict inequalities $f(\mathbf{x})$ is said to be strictly convex or strictly concave.

There are two further important properties of convex (concave) functions which can be deduced from equations 5.24 and 5.25.

If $f(\mathbf{x})$ is convex over the convex domain X and $\mathbf{x}_1, \mathbf{x}_2 \in X$, then

$$f(\mathbf{x}_2) \geqslant f(\mathbf{x}_1) + (\mathbf{x}_2 - \mathbf{x}_1)^{\mathrm{T}} \nabla f(\mathbf{x}_1). \tag{5.26}$$

The inequality is reversed for a concave function.

This is established by the following argument. Since $f(\mathbf{x})$ is convex, for $0 < \theta < 1$

$$f[\theta \mathbf{x}_2 + (1-\theta)\mathbf{x}_1] \leqslant \theta f(\mathbf{x}_2) + (1-\theta) f(\mathbf{x}_1)$$

$$\therefore \quad f[\mathbf{x}_1 + \theta(\mathbf{x}_2 - \mathbf{x}_1)] - f(\mathbf{x}_1) \leqslant \theta[f(\mathbf{x}_2) - f(\mathbf{x}_1)]$$

$$\therefore \quad f(\mathbf{x}_2) \geqslant f(\mathbf{x}_1) + \frac{f[\mathbf{x}_1 + \theta(\mathbf{x}_2 - \mathbf{x}_1)] - f(\mathbf{x}_1)}{\theta}.$$

But by the first mean value theorem

$$f[\mathbf{x}_1 + \theta(\mathbf{x}_2 - \mathbf{x}_1)] = f(\mathbf{x}_1) + \theta(\mathbf{x}_2 - \mathbf{x}_1)^{\mathrm{T}} \nabla f[\mathbf{x}_1 + \lambda\theta(\mathbf{x}_2 - \mathbf{x}_1)]$$

where λ is some value in $0 < \lambda < 1$; i.e. the derivative is evaluated at some point between $\mathbf{x}_1$ and $\mathbf{x}_1 + \theta(\mathbf{x}_2 - \mathbf{x}_1)$.

$$\therefore \quad f(\mathbf{x}_2) \geqslant f(\mathbf{x}_1) + (\mathbf{x}_2 - \mathbf{x}_1)^{\mathrm{T}} \nabla f[\mathbf{x}_1 + \theta\lambda(\mathbf{x}_2 - \mathbf{x}_1)].$$

As $\theta \to 0$ we obtain the result (equation 5.26).

For convex functions of one (two) variable(s) equation 5.26 says that such a function lies above any tangent line (plane) to the function (see Fig. 5.5).

A function is convex if the Hessian matrix

$$\mathbf{H} = \left(\frac{\partial^2 f}{\partial x_i\, \partial x_j}\right)$$

is positive definite. By Taylor's theorem we can write

$$f(\mathbf{x}) = f(\mathbf{x}_1) + (\mathbf{x} - \mathbf{x}_1)^{\mathrm{T}} \nabla f(\mathbf{x}_1) + \tfrac{1}{2}(\mathbf{x} - \mathbf{x}_1)^{\mathrm{T}} \mathbf{H}(\mathbf{x} - \mathbf{x}_1)$$

where $\mathbf{H}$ is evaluated at the point $\mathbf{x}_1 + \lambda(\mathbf{x} - \mathbf{x}_1)$ and $0 < \lambda < 1$.

Thus we really have to show that a positive definite quadratic function $\frac{1}{2}\mathbf{x}^{\mathrm{T}}\mathbf{H}\mathbf{x}$ is convex. This is not difficult. Let $\mathbf{x}_2$ and $\mathbf{x}_1$ be any values for $\mathbf{x}$ and let $\bar{\mathbf{x}} = \theta\mathbf{x}_2 + (1-\theta)\mathbf{x}_1, 0 < \theta < 1$.

Then

$$\begin{aligned}
&\bar{\mathbf{x}}^{\mathrm{T}} \mathbf{H}\bar{\mathbf{x}} - \theta \mathbf{x}_2^{\mathrm{T}} \mathbf{H}\mathbf{x}_2 - (1-\theta)\mathbf{x}_1^{\mathrm{T}} \mathbf{H}\mathbf{x}_1 \\
&\quad = \theta^2 \mathbf{x}_2^{\mathrm{T}} \mathbf{H}\mathbf{x}_2 + 2\theta(1-\theta)\mathbf{x}_2^{\mathrm{T}} \mathbf{H}\mathbf{x}_1 + (1-\theta)^2 \mathbf{x}_1^{\mathrm{T}} \mathbf{H}\mathbf{x}_1 - \theta \mathbf{x}_2^{\mathrm{T}} \mathbf{H}\mathbf{x}_2 - (1-\theta)\mathbf{x}_1^{\mathrm{T}} \mathbf{H}\mathbf{x}_1 \\
&\quad = -\theta(1-\theta)(\mathbf{x}_2 - \mathbf{x}_1)^{\mathrm{T}} \mathbf{H}(\mathbf{x}_2 - \mathbf{x}_1).
\end{aligned}$$

Since $0 < \theta < 1$, $(1 - \theta) > 0$ and so if $\mathbf{H}$ is positive definite the final expression is less than or equal to zero. Thus

$$[\theta \mathbf{x}_2 + (1 - \theta)\,\mathbf{x}_1]^{\mathrm{T}}\,\mathbf{H}[\theta \mathbf{x}_2 + (1 - \theta)\,\mathbf{x}_1] \leqslant \theta \mathbf{x}_2^{\mathrm{T}}\,\mathbf{H}\mathbf{x}_2 + (1 - \theta)\,\mathbf{x}_1^{\mathrm{T}}\,\mathbf{H}\mathbf{x}_1. \qquad (5.27)$$

For convex functions of one variable this says that the second derivative is non-negative so that the first derivative is an increasing function which can only be zero at one point. Thus such a function will have one minimum point.

Example 1

If $g_i(\mathbf{x})$, $(i = 1, 2, \ldots, m)$, are convex functions over the convex domain X, show that $\sum \lambda_i g_i(\mathbf{x})$ where the $\lambda_i \geqslant 0$ is also convex.

Let

$$h(\mathbf{x}) = \sum_{i=1}^{m} \lambda_i g_i(\mathbf{x}).$$

Then if $\mathbf{x}_1, \mathbf{x}_2 \in X$

$$\begin{aligned} h[\theta \mathbf{x}_2 + (1 - \theta)\,\mathbf{x}_1] &= \sum_{i=1}^{m} \lambda_i g_i[\theta \mathbf{x}_2 + (1 - \theta)\,\mathbf{x}_1] \\ &\leqslant \sum_{i=1}^{m} \lambda_i[\theta g_i(\mathbf{x}_2) + (1 - \theta)\,g(\mathbf{x}_1)] \\ &\leqslant \theta \sum_{i=1}^{m} \lambda_i g_i(\mathbf{x}_2) + (1 - \theta) \sum_{i=1}^{m} \lambda_i g_i(\mathbf{x}_1) \\ &= \theta h(\mathbf{x}_2) + (1 - \theta)\,h(\mathbf{x}_1) \end{aligned}$$

which proves $h(\mathbf{x})$ to be convex.

Example 2

If the constraint region is defined by $g_i(\mathbf{x}) \leqslant b_i$, $(i = 1, \ldots, m)$ where the $g_i(\mathbf{x})$ are convex functions show that the constraint region is convex.

Suppose $\mathbf{x}_1$ and $\mathbf{x}_2$ are feasible points within the constraint region. Then

$$\begin{aligned} g_i(\mathbf{x}_1) &\leqslant b_i \quad i = 1, \ldots, m \\ g_i(\mathbf{x}_2) &\leqslant b_i \quad i = 1, \ldots, m. \end{aligned}$$

Then, if $0 < \theta < 1$, for $i = 1, 2, \ldots, m$

$$\begin{aligned} g_i[\theta \mathbf{x}_2 + (1 - \theta)\,\mathbf{x}_1] &\leqslant \theta g_i(\mathbf{x}_2) + (1 - \theta)\,g_i(\mathbf{x}_1) \\ &\leqslant \theta b_i + (1 - \theta)\,b_i \\ &= b_i. \end{aligned}$$

Thus $\theta \mathbf{x}_2 + (1 - \theta)\,\mathbf{x}_1$ belongs to the set of feasible points which is thus a convex set.

We can use the results above to establish the theorem that if $f(\mathbf{x})$ is a convex function over the region constrained by $g_i(\mathbf{x}) \leqslant b_i$, where the $g_i(\mathbf{x})$ are convex, then a local minimum of $f(\mathbf{x})$ in this region is its global minimum in this region.

For suppose $\mathbf{x}^*$ is the global minimum and $\mathbf{x}_0$ is a local minimum with $f(\mathbf{x}^*) < f(\mathbf{x}_0)$. Both these points are feasible and since the feasible region is convex and $f(\mathbf{x})$ is convex

$$\begin{aligned} f[\theta\mathbf{x}^* + (1-\theta)\,\mathbf{x}_0] &\leqslant \theta f(\mathbf{x}^*) + (1-\theta)\,f(\mathbf{x}_0) \\ &\leqslant \theta f(\mathbf{x}_0) + (1-\theta)\,f(\mathbf{x}_0) \\ &\leqslant f(\mathbf{x}_0) \end{aligned}$$

for $0 < \theta < 1$.

But if θ is sufficiently small $\theta\mathbf{x}^* + (1-\theta)\,\mathbf{x}_0$ lies within δ of $\mathbf{x}_0$. Thus since $\mathbf{x}_0$ is a local minimum it is not possible for the function value at the first point to be less than $f(\mathbf{x}_0)$. Thus we have a contradiction and $\mathbf{x}^*$ and $\mathbf{x}_0$ must coincide.

Example 3

Write down the Kuhn–Tucker conditions for the problem: minimise $-x^2 - y^2$ subject to $x, y \geqslant 0$, $x + 2y \leqslant 3$. The Lagrange function is

$$F(x, y, \boldsymbol{\lambda}, \mathbf{u}) = -x^2 - y^2 + \lambda_1(-x + u_1^2) + \lambda_2(-y + u_2^2) + \lambda_3(x + 2y + u_3^2 - 3).$$

The necessary conditions are:

$$-2x - \lambda_1 + \lambda_3 = 0$$

$$-2y - \lambda_2 + 2\lambda_3 = 0$$

$$\lambda_1 x = 0, \quad \lambda_2 y = 0, \quad \lambda_3(x + 2y - 3) = 0$$

$$x + 2y \leqslant 3$$

$$\lambda_1, \lambda_2, \lambda_3 \geqslant 0.$$

We try to find solutions for these conditions. If $x, y > 0$ then $\lambda_1 = \lambda_2 = 0$.

(a) If $\lambda_3 = 0$ then $x = y = 0$ and we have a maximum.

(b) If $\lambda_1 = \lambda_2 = 0$, $\lambda_3 > 0$, then $2x = \lambda_3 = y$ and $x + 2y - 3 = 0$. Thus $x = \frac{3}{5}$ and $y = \frac{6}{5}$ and $\lambda_3 = \frac{6}{5}$, all conditions are satisfied and

$$f = -\tfrac{45}{25}.$$

(c) If $\lambda_1 > 0$, $\lambda_2 = 0$, $\lambda_3 > 0$ then

$$x = 0, \quad y > 0, \quad x + 2y = 3 \quad \text{i.e. } y = \tfrac{3}{2}.$$

$$\therefore \quad \lambda_3 = \tfrac{3}{2}, \quad \lambda_1 = \tfrac{3}{2} \quad \text{and all conditions are satisfied.}$$

$$f = -\tfrac{9}{4}.$$

(d) If $\lambda_1 = 0$, $\lambda_2 > 0$, $\lambda_3 > 0$ then

$$x > 0, \quad y = 0, \quad x + 2y = 3, \quad \text{i.e. } x = 3, \quad \lambda_3 = 6, \quad \lambda_2 = 12$$

and all conditions are satisfied and $f = -9$.

Hence there are several points which satisfy the necessary conditions. The global minimum is -9 at $(3, 0)$. The problem is illustrated in Fig. 5.6.

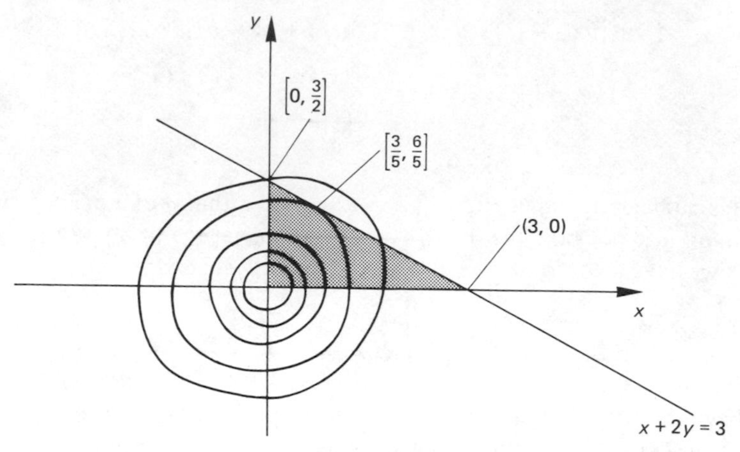

Figure 5.6

The difficulty that arises in Example 3 is removed if $f(\mathbf{x})$ is convex and the constraint region is convex. For the problem, minimise $f(\mathbf{x})$ subject to $g_i(\mathbf{x}) \leqslant b_i$, where $f(\mathbf{x})$ is convex and the $g_i(\mathbf{x})$ are convex, the Kuhn–Tucker necessary conditions (equation 5.23) are also sufficient.

For in this case the Lagrange function (equation 5.16)

$$F(\mathbf{x}, \boldsymbol{\lambda}, \mathbf{u}) = f(\mathbf{x}) + \sum_{i=1}^{m} \lambda_i [g_i(\mathbf{x}) + u_i^2 - b_i]$$

being the sum of convex functions is also convex. The λ_i are of course non-negative. Hence F has a global minimum at the point where its derivatives vanish and there is only one such point. Thus the necessary conditions are also sufficient.

Example 3 does not contradict this result. The $g_i(\mathbf{x})$ are certainly convex but $f(x, y) = -(x^2 + y^2)$ is *not* convex: it is concave.

5.4 References

1 B. Bernholtz, 'A new derivation of the Kuhn–Tucker conditions', *Operations Research*, **12**, No. 2, 295–299, 1964.

2 H. W. Kuhn and A. W. Tucker, 'Non Linear Programming', in *Proc. of 2nd Berkeley Symposium on Mathematical Statistics and Probability* (Editor J. Neyman), Berkeley, University of California Press, 481–492, 1951.

3 G. R. Walsh, *Methods of Optimisation*, John Wiley, 1975.

4 D. J. Wilde, 'Differential Calculus in Non Linear Programming', *Operations Research* **10**, No. 6, 764–773, 1962.

5 P. Wolfe, 'Methods of Non Linear Programming' in *Recent Advances in Mathematical Programming* (Editors R. L. Graves and P. Wolfe), McGraw-Hill, New York, 67–86, 1963.

6 P. Wolfe, 'Methods of Non Linear Programming' in *Non Linear Programming* (Editor J. Abadie), Nato Summer School, Menton, 1964, North Holland Publishing Co., Amsterdam, 1967.

Exercises 5

1 Show that $f(x_1,x_2) = x_1^2 + x_2^2$ where $x_1x_2 = 4$ has a minimum value of 8 when $(x_1, x_2) = (\pm 2, \pm 2)$.

2 Show that $f(x, y) = x^2 + y^2$ where x and y are constrained by $x - y = 5$ has a minimum when $x = 2{\cdot}5, y = -2{\cdot}5$.

3 If a, b, c, k are positive constants, find positive x, y, z such that $x + y + z = k$ and $w = ax^2 + by^2 + cz^2$ is a minimum.

4 If a, b, c are all negative and

$$f(x_1, x_2, x_3) = ax_2x_3 + bx_3x_1 + cx_1x_2$$

where in addition $x_1 + x_2 + x_3 = 1$, show that $f(x_1, x_2, x_3)$ has a minimum value of $abc/[2(ab + bc + ca) - (a^2 + b^2 + c^2)]$, provided the denominator above is positive.

5 Find the stationary value(s) of xy^2z^3 if $x + y + z = 6$.

6 An open rectangular box made of thin sheet metal has height z, and a rectangular base of dimensions x, y. The base and the sides of length x are of thickness d (small) and the sides of length y are of thickness $2d$. If the quantity of material is fixed, show that the volume of the box is a maximum when $x = 2y = 4z$.

7 Find the Kuhn–Tucker conditions for the problem:

$$\text{minimise} \quad x^2 + y^2$$

$$\text{subject to} \quad x \geqslant 0, \quad y \geqslant 0, \quad x + y \geqslant 5$$

and hence solve this problem.

8 Find the Kuhn–Tucker conditions for the problem:

$$\text{minimise} \quad f(x, y) = x^2 + 6xy - 4x - 2y$$

$$\text{subject to} \quad x^2 + 2y \leqslant 1$$

$$2x - 2y \leqslant 1.$$

Hence solve this problem.

9 If $f(\mathbf{x})$ is a convex function on the domain X show that $g(\mathbf{x}) = -af(\mathbf{x})$ where a is positive is a concave function on X.

10 The functions $g_i(\mathbf{x})$, $i = 1, 2, \ldots, m$ are all convex. Show that the set of points $\{\mathbf{x}: g_i(\mathbf{x}) \leqslant k\}$ where k is a constant form a convex set.

11 $h(x)$ is a positive concave function of x for $a \leqslant x \leqslant b$. By considering its second derivative or otherwise show that $g(x) = 1/h(x)$ is a convex function for $a \leqslant x \leqslant b$.

Generalise this result to the case where $h(\mathbf{x})$ is a positive concave function on the domain X. Show that the Hessian matrix of $g(\mathbf{x}) = 1/h(\mathbf{x})$ is positive definite.

12 Consider the problem of minimising the convex function $f(\mathbf{x})$ subject to the constraints $g_i(\mathbf{x}) \leqslant 0$, $i = 1, 2, \ldots, m$. Suppose that the unconstrained minimum of $f(\mathbf{x})$ is at $\mathbf{x}^*$ and that $g_1(\mathbf{x}^*), g_2(\mathbf{x}^*), g_3(\mathbf{x}^*) > 0$. If the constrained minimum is at $\mathbf{x}_0$, show that at least one of $g_1(\mathbf{x}_0)$, $g_2(\mathbf{x}_0)$, $g_3(\mathbf{x}_0)$ is zero. Explain the geometrical significance of this result.

13 Find the maximum and minimum values of

$$x^2 + y^2$$

if $3x^2 + 4xy + 6y^2 = 140$. Interpret the result geometrically.

14 The problem of minimising economic lot sizes can be expressed as one of minimising the function

$$f(x_1, x_2) = \frac{\alpha}{x_1} + \frac{\beta}{x_2} + \gamma(x_1 + x_2),$$

where $x_1, x_2 \geqslant 0$. α and β are constants connected with the set-up costs for production runs of the two commodities and γ is a constant connected to the cost of holding stock. (See Question 8, Exercise 1.)

Show that this function is minimised if $x_1 = \sqrt{\alpha/\gamma}$, $x_2 = \sqrt{\beta/\gamma}$.

In reality storage facilities mean that x_1 and x_2 must satisfy in addition $x_1 + x_2 \leqslant S$ where S is some constant.

Write down the Kuhn–Tucker conditions for the resulting problem and hence obtain a solution.

15 A parcel to be sent through the mail has a cuboid shape with dimensions x_1, x_2, x_3. The post office stipulates that $x_1 \leqslant 20$, $x_2 \leqslant 11$, $x_3 \leqslant 42$ and in addition $x_1 + 2x_2 + 2x_3 \leqslant 72$. Find the dimensions which maximise the volume. [This is Rosenbrock's *modified* Post Office Parcel Problem. See also the next chapter.]

16 The standard Post Office Parcel Problem is similar to the above except that the constraints are

$$x_i \leqslant 42, \quad (i = 1, 2, 3), \quad x_1 + 2x_2 + 2x_3 \leqslant 72.$$

Write down the Kuhn–Tucker conditions for this problem and hence obtain the solution.

6

Search Methods

6.1 Modified Hooke and Jeeves

We first discuss methods of solving the non-linear programming problem which only use function values. The direct search methods of Chapter 3, when applied to the unconstrained optimisation problem, were successful. One might suppose that they could be modified to take account of constraints. Indeed it has been suggested that merely giving the objective function a very large value (in a minimisation problem) whenever the constraints are violated will suffice. Certainly this idea has an obvious intuitive appeal and is easy to program.

For each trial point we check whether it lies within the constraint region. If so we evaluate the objective function in the normal way. If not we give the objective function a very large value. In this way the search method will be directed back into the feasible region and hence towards the minimum point within the feasible region.

To illustrate an attempt to implement this procedure we give a listing of a modified Hooke and Jeeves direct search program. The problem being considered is the following.

$$\text{Minimise} \quad f(x_1, x_2) = 3x_1^2 + 4x_1 x_2 + 5x_2^2$$

$$\text{subject to} \quad x_1 \geqslant 0, \quad x_2 \geqslant 0, \quad x_1 + x_2 \geqslant 4.$$

(See Example 1 of Section 5.2.)

The program is identical with the Hooke and Jeeves program in Section 3.2 except that the subroutine at 2ØØØ has been modified to take account of the constraints in the way just outlined. The minimum is 44 at (3, 1) on the constraint $x_1 + x_2 = 4$.

```
READY.

 1Ø PRINT"CONSTRAINED HOOKE & JEEVES"
 2Ø REM Z=F(X1,X2,...,XN) AT 2ØØØ
 3Ø PRINT"NUMBER OF VARIABLES":INPUT N
 4Ø DIM X(N),B(N),Y(N),P(N)
 5Ø PRINT"INITIAL POINT X1,X2,..XN"
 6Ø FOR I=1 TO N:INPUT X(I):NEXT I
 7Ø PRINT"STEP LENGTH":INPUT H
 8Ø K=H
 9Ø FOR I=1 TO N
 1ØØ Y(I)=X(I):P(I)=X(I):B(I)=X(I):NEXT I
 11Ø GOSUB 2ØØØ:FI=Z
 12Ø PRINT "INITIAL VALUE"Z
 13Ø FOR I=1 TO N:PRINT X(I),:NEXT I:PRINT""
 14Ø PS=Ø:BS=1
 15Ø REM EXPLORE ABOUT BASE POINT
 18Ø J=1:FB=FI
```

```
 200 X(J)=Y(J)+K
 210 GOSUB 2000
 220 IF Z<FI THEN GOTO 280
 230 X(J)=Y(J)-K
 240 GOSUB 2000
 250 IF Z<FI THEN GOTO 280
 260 X(J)=Y(J)
 270 GOTO 290
 280 Y(J)=X(J)
 290 GOSUB 2000
 300 FI=Z
 310 PRINT"EXPLORATION STEP"Z
 320 FOR I=1 TO N:PRINT X(I),:NEXT I:PRINT""
 330 IF J=N THEN GOTO 360
 340 J=J+1
 350 GOTO 200
 360 IF FI<FB-1E-08 THEN GOTO 540
 370 REM AFTER 360 MAKE A PATTERN MOVE IF FUNCTION HAS BEEN REDUCED
 380 IF PS=1 AND BS=0 THEN GOTO 420
 390 REM BUT IF EXPLORATION WAS ABOUT A PATTERN PT.
 395 REM AND NO REDUCTION WAS MADE CHANGE BASE AT 420
 400 REM OTHERWISE REDUCE STEP LENGTH AT 490
 410 GOTO 490
 420 FOR I=1 TO N:P(I)=B(I):Y(I)=B(I):X(I)=B(I):NEXT I
 430 GOSUB 2000:BS=1:PS=0
 440 FI=Z:FB=Z
 450 PRINT"BASE CHANGE"Z
 460 FOR I=1 TO N:PRINT X(I),:NEXT I:PRINT""
 470 REM (FOLLOW ON FROM 395)AND EXPLORE ABOUT NEW BASE POINT
 480 J=1:GOTO 200
 490 K=K/10
 500 PRINT"CONTRACT STEP LENGTH"
 510 IF K<1E-08 THEN GOTO 700
 520 REM IF WE HAVE NOT FINISHED MAKE NEW
 525 REM EXPLORATION ABOUT LATEST BASE POINT
 530 J=1: GOTO 200
 535 REM PATTERN MOVE
 540 FOR I=1 TO N:P(I)=2*Y(I)-B(I)
 550 B(I)=Y(I):X(I)=P(I):Y(I)=X(I)
 560 NEXT I
 570 GOSUB 2000:FB=FI:PS=1:BS=0:FI=Z
 580 PRINT"PATTERN MOVE"Z
 590 FOR I=1 TO N:PRINT X(I),:NEXT I:PRINT""
 600 REM THEN EXPLORE ABOUT LATEST PATTERN POINT
 610 J=1:GOTO 200
 700 PRINT"      MINIMUM FOUND"
 710 FOR I=1 TO N:PRINT"X"I"="P(I):NEXT I:PRINT""
 750 PRINT"FUNCTION MINIMUM="FB
 760 PRINT"NO. OF FUNCTION EVALUATIONS="FE
 790 END
 2000 IF X(1)<0 THEN Z=1E30:GOTO 2150
 2010 IF X(2)<0 THEN Z=1E30:GOTO 2150
 2020 IF X(1)+X(2)<4 THEN Z=1E30:GOTO 2150
 2100 Z=3*X(1)*X(1)+4*X(1)*X(2)+5*X(2)*X(2)
 2140 REM COUNT FUNCTION EVALUATIONS
 2150 FE=FE+1
 2200 RETURN
READY.
```

With initial point (4, 3) and step length 1 the output given was obtained and the program was successful.

```
CONSTRAINED HOOKE & JEEVES
NUMBER OF VARIABLES              2
INITIAL POINT X1,X2,..XN         4,3
STEP LENGTH                      1



INITIAL VALUE 141
 4             3
EXPLORATION STEP 1Ø8
 3             3
EXPLORATION STEP 71
 3             2
PATTERN MOVE 1E+3Ø
 2             1
EXPLORATION STEP 44
 3             1
EXPLORATION STEP 44
 3             1
PATTERN MOVE 1E+3Ø
 3             Ø
EXPLORATION STEP 48
 4             Ø
EXPLORATION STEP 48
 4             Ø
BASE CHANGE 44
 3             1
EXPLORATION STEP 44
 3             1
EXPLORATION STEP 44
 3             1
CONTRACT STEP LENGTH
EXPLORATION STEP 44
 3             1
EXPLORATION STEP 44
 3             1
CONTRACT STEP LENGTH
EXPLORATION STEP 44
 3             1
EXPLORATION STEP 44
 3             1
CONTRACT STEP LENGTH
EXPLORATION STEP 44
 3             1
EXPLORATION STEP 44
 3             1
CONTRACT STEP LENGTH
EXPLORATION STEP 44
 3             1
EXPLORATION STEP 44
 3             1
CONTRACT STEP LENGTH
EXPLORATION STEP 44
 3             1
EXPLORATION STEP 44
 3             1
CONTRACT STEP LENGTH
EXPLORATION STEP 44
 3             1
EXPLORATION STEP 44
 3             1
CONTRACT STEP LENGTH
EXPLORATION STEP 44
 3             1
```

```
EXPLORATION STEP 44
 3            1
CONTRACT STEP LENGTH
EXPLORATION STEP 44
 3            1
EXPLORATION STEP 44
 3            1
CONTRACT STEP LENGTH
       MINIMUM FOUND
X 1 = 3
X 2 = 1

FUNCTION MINIMUM= 44
NO. OF FUNCTION EVALUATIONS= 74
```

With initial point (3, 4) and step length 1 the program succeeded.

With initial point (5, 6) and step length 1 the program 'got stuck' at the point (1, 3) on the active constraint and got the wrong answer. The output is given

```
CONSTRAINED HOOKE & JEEVES
NUMBER OF VARIABLES              2
INITIAL POINT X1,X2,..XN         5,6
STEP LENGTH                      1



INITIAL VALUE 375
 5             6
EXPLORATION STEP 324
 4             6
EXPLORATION STEP 253
 4             5
PATTERN MOVE 155
 3             4
EXPLORATION STEP 124
 2             4
EXPLORATION STEP 81
 2             3
PATTERN MOVE 1E+30
 0             1
EXPLORATION STEP 1E+30
 0             1
EXPLORATION STEP 1E+30
 0             1
BASE CHANGE 81
 2             3
EXPLORATION STEP 60
 1             3
EXPLORATION STEP 60
 1             3
PATTERN MOVE 1E+30
 0             3
EXPLORATION STEP 60
 1             3
EXPLORATION STEP 60
 1             3
BASE CHANGE 60
 1             3
EXPLORATION STEP 60
 1             3
```

```
EXPLORATION STEP 6Ø
 1          3
CONTRACT STEP LENGTH
EXPLORATION STEP 6Ø
 1          3
EXPLORATION STEP 6Ø
 1          3
CONTRACT STEP LENGTH
EXPLORATION STEP 6Ø
 1          3
EXPLORATION STEP 6Ø
 1          3
CONTRACT STEP LENGTH
EXPLORATION STEP 6Ø
 1          3
EXPLORATION STEP 6Ø
 1          3
CONTRACT STEP LENGTH
EXPLORATION STEP 6Ø
 1          3
EXPLORATION STEP 6Ø
 1          3
CONTRACT STEP LENGTH
EXPLORATION STEP 6Ø
 1          3
EXPLORATION STEP 6Ø
 1          3
CONTRACT STEP LENGTH
EXPLORATION STEP 6Ø
 1          3
EXPLORATION STEP 6Ø
 1          3
CONTRACT STEP LENGTH
EXPLORATION STEP 6Ø
 1          3
EXPLORATION STEP 6Ø
 1          3
CONTRACT STEP LENGTH
EXPLORATION STEP 6Ø
 1          3
EXPLORATION STEP 6Ø
 1          3
CONTRACT STEP LENGTH
     MINIMUM FOUND
X 1 = 1
X 2 = 3

FUNCTION MINIMUM= 6Ø
NO. OF FUNCTION EVALUATIONS= 89
```

Similarly frustrating results were obtained with initial point (5, 6) and step length 0·5. A false solution was obtained at (1·5, 2·5). With initial point (4, 3) but a step length not of 1, which worked, but of 0·5, the false solution (2·5, 1·5) was obtained.

The problem is clear. The method is not able to move along the constraint and converges on the first point on the constraint that it locates as the solution. As was stressed in Chapter 5, the general constrained optimisation problem is a hard problem and more sophisticated procedures than this will be needed to obtain a practical solution method.

6.2 The Complex Method

Difficulties encountered in trying to implement the search methods then in existence, prompted Box in 1964 to devise his own method. Essentially it is a modification of the Simplex Method of Nelder and Mead so as to take account of constraints. Box called it the Complex Method.

The problem considered is that of minimising $f(\mathbf{x}) = f(x_1, x_2, \ldots, x_n)$ where the $\mathbf{x}$ are subject to the *explicit* constraints

$$l_j \leqslant x_j \leqslant u_j, \quad j = 1, 2, \ldots, n \tag{6.1}$$

and also the *implicit* constraints

$$g_i(\mathbf{x}) \leqslant b_i, \quad i = 1, 2, \ldots, m. \tag{6.2}$$

If the objective function $f(\mathbf{x})$ is convex and the implicit constraints $g_i(\mathbf{x})$ are convex the problem will have a unique solution. The l_j and u_j are lower and upper bounds for the variables. If in the actual problem certain variables are in theory unbounded, assuming 'safe' bounds which certainly include the optimum will enable the method to be implemented.

The method is an iterative procedure. It assumes that we know n and m, the l_j and the u_j and have an initial point $\mathbf{x}_1$ that satisfies all the constraints (equations 6.1 and 6.2). We first have to generate a set of k points which satisfy the constraints, and evaluate the objective function at those k points. This set of points is called a complex. Box found that k needed to be larger than $n + 1$, the number of points used in the Simplex Method of Nelder and Mead. He suggested the value $k = 2n$.

As we have mentioned it is assumed that $\mathbf{x}_1$, satisfying all the constraints is given. We can generate further points which satisfy equation 6.1 by

$$x_{ij} = l_j + r(u_j - l_j) \tag{6.3}$$

for $j = 1, 2, \ldots, n$ and $i = 2, 3, \ldots, k$ where r is a pseudo-random rectangularly distributed variable on the range (0, 1). Such variables are obtained from the statement Y = RND(X) in BASIC.

Points generated by equation 6.3 for a given value of j will automatically satisfy equation 6.1. If they also satisfy equation 6.2 they are accepted as points of the initial complex. If the point generated by equation 6.3 does not satisfy equation 6.2 we move it half way towards the centroid of already accepted points, i.e. we form

$$\mathbf{x}_i' = \frac{(\mathbf{x}_i + \mathbf{x}_c)}{2} \tag{6.4}$$

where

$$\mathbf{x}_c = \frac{1}{i-1} \sum_{e=1}^{i-1} \mathbf{x}_e. \tag{6.5}$$

If equation 6.4 is still not feasible we repeat this procedure again and again until it is. If the $g_i(\mathbf{x})$ are convex we will ultimately satisfy the constraints. Of course since $\mathbf{x}_1$ is in the constrained region we will always have a centroid of already accepted points.

In this way we obtain our initial complex of feasible points. It is convenient to order these points according to the magnitude of the corresponding function values. We can describe the procedure for the initialisation of the process by means of a flow chart. In the program listing this is executed by the statements up to line 1ØØØ.

Flow Chart to Initiate the Complex Method

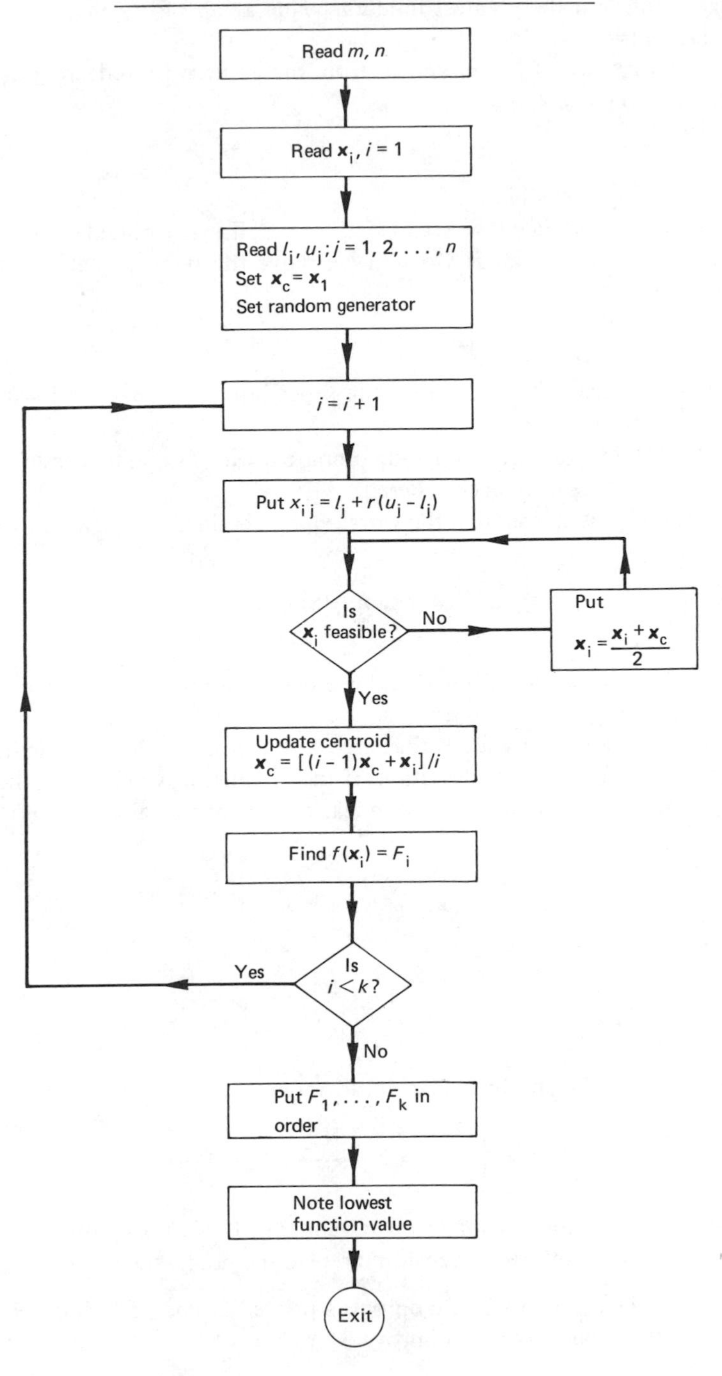

We now come to the iterative procedure of the Complex Method in which we seek to move towards the minimum point within the constrained region. The steps required are outlined below.

1 Find the point with the greatest function value $\mathbf{x}_h$ and form the centroid $\mathbf{x}_0$ of the other $(k-1)$ points.
2 We try to move away from $\mathbf{x}_h$ and so form the point $\mathbf{x}_r$ by reflecting $\mathbf{x}_h$ in $\mathbf{x}_0$, using a reflection factor $\alpha\,(>1)$.

$$\text{i.e.}\quad \mathbf{x}_r = (1+\alpha)\,\mathbf{x}_0 - \alpha\mathbf{x}_h \tag{6.6}$$

3 We next test if $\mathbf{x}_r$ is feasible.
(i) If not and if l_j is violated we set $x_{rj} = l_j + 10^{-6}$; if u_j is violated set $x_{rj} = u_j - 10^{-6}$.
(ii) If an implicit constraint is violated we move the point $\mathbf{x}_r$ halfway towards the centroid $\mathbf{x}_0$

$$\text{i.e.}\quad \mathbf{x}_r(\text{new}) = (\mathbf{x}_r + \mathbf{x}_0)/2 \tag{6.7}$$

We then retest for feasibility and repeat the procedures at step 3 until a feasible point is obtained.
4 If $\mathbf{x}_r$ is feasible we evaluate $f(\mathbf{x}_r)$ and compare it with $f(\mathbf{x}_k)$ the worst function value since the function values have been ordered.

If $f(\mathbf{x}_r) > f(\mathbf{x}_k)$ i.e. is worse than the worst value obtained so far we move $\mathbf{x}_r$ halfway towards $\mathbf{x}_0$

$$\text{i.e.}\quad \mathbf{x}_r(\text{new}) = (\mathbf{x}_r + \mathbf{x}_0)/2,$$

and then return to step 3.
5 If $f(\mathbf{x}_r) < f(\mathbf{x}_k)$ we replace $\mathbf{x}_k$ by $\mathbf{x}_r$ and reorder the points and function values of the complex.
6 We next calculate two quantities that are used to test whether the method has converged. These are the standard deviation of the k function values, and the maximum distance d_m between two points of the complex. The former is calculated as

$$\sigma = \left\{ \sum_{e=1}^{k} [f(\mathbf{x}_e) - \bar{f}]^2/k \right\}^{1/2} \tag{6.8}$$

where

$$\bar{f} = \frac{1}{k} \sum_{e=1}^{k} f(\mathbf{x}_e) \tag{6.9}$$

but σ^2 is best calculated from the equivalent formula

$$\sigma^2 = \left\{ \sum_{e=1}^{k} f(\mathbf{x}_e)^2 - \frac{[\sum f(\mathbf{x})]^2}{k} \right\} \Big/ k \tag{6.10}$$

7 The test of convergence is made on σ^2 and d_m. If *both* are sufficiently small we terminate. Otherwise we return to step 1 and repeat the process.

In the program listed, intermediate output is printed at line 35ØØ but only if the best (minimum) function value has been improved.

A flow chart indicating the steps 1 to 7 is given and takes the program through to line 38ØØ. The statements from 4ØØØ–41ØØ merely give the final solution after convergence.

The objective function is evaluated at subroutine 5ØØØ. The constraints are tested at subroutine 6ØØØ. IC = 1 indicates the violation of an implicit constraint, EC = 1

The Iterative Routine of the Complex Method

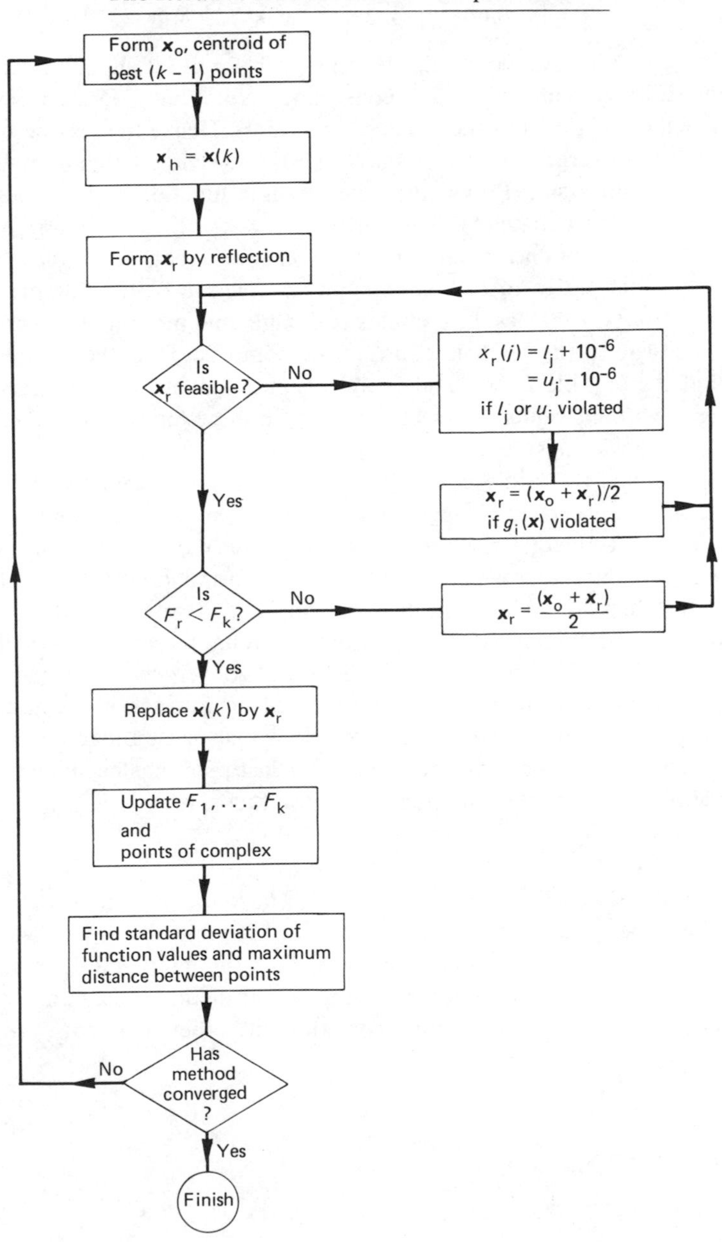

the violation of an explicit constraint. The arrays EC(J), J = 1, 2, ..., 2N and IC(L), L = 1, ..., M indicate the particular constraints, if any, that have been violated.

The subroutines listed are appropriate to the modified Post Office Parcel Problem (see Exercises 5, question 15);

$$\text{minimise} \quad f(\mathbf{x}) = -x_1 x_2 x_3$$

$$\text{subject to} \quad 0 \leqslant x_1 \leqslant 20, \quad 0 \leqslant x_2 \leqslant 11, \quad 0 \leqslant x_3 \leqslant 42$$

$$\text{and} \quad x_1 + 2x_2 + 2x_3 \leqslant 72.$$

There is only one implicit constraint for this problem but it should be clear how the subroutine would be modified for other constraints. Note that if IM is 1 when we enter the subroutine then we only test the implicit constraints. Hence the reason for line 64Ø.

The procedure converges when the complex shrinks to lying within a small neighbourhood of the minimum point. Provided the variation in function values is also small the convergence test will terminate at this stage.

The choice of $k = 2n$ and $\alpha = 1{\cdot}3$ (see line 112Ø) are empirical rules suggested by Box. The former is partly to prevent premature collapse of the complex. The over-reflection factor $\alpha\,(>1)$ enables the complex to expand and move in the desired direction. The moves halfway to the centroid contract the complex. Thus the complex is able to move around the feasible region and is able to move along a constraint and turn a corner where two constraints intersect. The device of setting the variables just inside their bounds helps with this.

The way in which the initial complex is generated means that several runs can be made very easily. It is certainly suggested that more than one run should be made, just in case the method converges prematurely by some quirk of the particular points used. Indeed, it is probably a good idea to obtain some information on the likely magnitude of the minimum function value, and then subtract this at subroutine 5ØØØ so that, for the function actually minimised, the minimum is roughly zero. This will avoid any problems when calculating the variance at the test of convergence. After all if the values were 9 digit values with the first 8 the same we could run into serious accuracy problems and might even obtain a negative variance!! (It would just be machine accuracy but would cause an execution error nonetheless.) This last point has been incorporated into subroutine 5ØØØ. As stated the minimum value is in fact zero.

Example 1

Solve the modified Post Office Parcel Problem. The initial point used was (20, 10, 10). The random number generator was initialised with 7199 but this is irrelevant. The first and last parts of the computer output are given. The true minimum occurs at the point (20, 11, 15) so we have obtained good accuracy by our method. The number of function evaluations at 231, is fairly high (compared with many other runs that were made), but is in line with the results obtained by Box.

```
READY.

 2Ø PRINT"COMPLEX METHOD":PRINT""
 4Ø REM Z=F(X1,X2...XN) AT 5ØØØ
 6Ø REM G1,G2,...GM AND TEST OF SATISFACTION AT 6ØØØ
 8Ø PRINT"NO. OF CONSTRAINTS":INPUT M
```

```
100 PRINT"NO. OF VARIABLES":INPUT N
120 DIM X,Y,L,U,XC,XO,XR,XH(N)
160 K=2*N
180 DIM C(K,N),F(K),G(M),IC(M),EC(2*N)
200 PRINT"INITIAL VALUE"
220 FOR J=1 TO N:INPUT X(J):C(1,J)=X(J):XC(J)=X(J):NEXT J
240 REM READ LOWER & UPPER LIMITS
260 FOR J=1 TO N:READ L(J),U(J):NEXT J
280 REM SET RANDOM GENERATOR
290 PRINT"INPUT X":INPUT X
500 I=1
520 GOSUB 5000:F(1)=Z
600 I=I+1
620 FOR J=1 TO N:C(I,J)=L(J)+RND(X)*(U(J)-L(J)):X(J)=C(I,J):NEXT J
640 IM=1:GOSUB 6000
660 IF IC=1 THEN GOTO 720
670 REM UPDATE CENTROID
680 FOR J=1 TO N:XC(J)=((I-1)*XC(J)+C(I,J))/I:NEXT J
700 GOTO 760
720 FOR J=1 TO N:C(I,J)=(C(I,J)+XC(J))/2:X(J)=C(I,J):NEXT J
740 GOTO 640
760 GOSUB 5000:F(I)=Z
780 IF I<K THEN GOTO 600
790 REM PUT FUNCTION VALUES AND POINTS IN ORDER
800 FOR J=1 TO K-1
820 FOR I=J+1 TO K
840 IF F(J)<=F(I) THEN GOTO 900
860 F=F(J):F(J)=F(I):F(I)=F
880 FOR L=1 TO N:Y(L)=C(J,L):C(J,L)=C(I,L):C(I,L)=Y(L):NEXT L
900 NEXT I:NEXT J
910 REM NOTE LOWEST VALUE
920 FM=F(1)
1000 PRINT"FIRST POINT"
1020 PRINT"MIN. VALUE="F(1)
1040 PRINT"MIN. POINT"
1060 FOR L=1 TO N:PRINT"X"L,C(1,L):NEXT L
1080 PRINT""
1100 REM SET REFLECTION FACTOR
1120 A=1.3
1190 REM FORM CENTROID OF BEST (K-1) POINTS AND RECORD WORST POINT
1200 FOR L=1 TO N:XH(L)=C(K,L):XO(L)=(K*XC(L)-XH(L))/(K-1):NEXT L
1390 REM FORM REFLECTED POINT
1400 FOR L=1 TO N:XR(L)=(1+A)*XO(L)-A*XH(L):X(L)=XR(L):NEXT L
1490 REM TEST NEW POINT FOR FEASIBILITY
1500 IM=0
1520 GOSUB 6000
1540 IF EC=0 AND IC=0 THEN GOTO 2000
1550 REM IF POINT IS FEASIBLE GOTO 2000 AND FIND FUNCTION VALUE
1600 IF EC=0 THEN GOTO 1800
1610 REM IF EXPLICIT CONSTRAINTS VIOLATED
1615 REM RESET JUST INSIDE BOUNDARY
1620 FOR J=1 TO N
1640 IF EC(J)=1 THEN XR(J)=L(J)+1E-6:X(J)=XR(J)
1660 IF EC(J+N)=1 THEN XR(J)=U(J)-1E-6:X(J)=XR(J)
1680 NEXT J
1800 IF IC=0 THEN GOTO 2000
1810 REM IF IMPLICIT CONSTRAINT VIOLATED
1815 REM MOVE HALFWAY TO CENTROID XO
1820 FOR L=1 TO N:XR(L)=(XR(L)+XO(L))/2:X(L)=XR(L):NEXT L
1840 GOTO 1490
2000 GOSUB 5000:FR=Z
2010 REM IF NEW VALUE IS THE WORST MOVE HALFWAY TO XO AND TRY AGAIN
2020 IF FR<F(K) THEN GOTO 2400
2040 FOR L=1 TO N:XR(L)=(XR(L)+XO(L))/2:X(L)=XR(L):NEXT L
2060 GOTO 1490
```

```
 2400 REM UPDATE XC AND REPLACE WORST POINT BY NEW POINT
 2410 F(K)=FR
 2420 FOR L=1 TO N
 2440 XC(L)=K*XC(L)-C(K,L)+XR(L)
 2460 XC(L)=XC(L)/K:C(K,L)=XR(L)
 2480 NEXT L
 2490 REM PUT FUNCTION VALUES AND POINTS IN ORDER
 2500 FOR J=1 TO K-1
 2520 FOR I=J+1 TO K
 2540 IF F(J)<=F(I) THEN GOTO 2600
 2560 F=F(J):F(J)=F(I):F(I)=F
 2580 FOR L=1 TO N:Y(L)=C(J,L):C(J,L)=C(I,L):C(I,L)=Y(L):NEXT L
 2600 NEXT I:NEXT J
 2610 REM IF LOWEST VALUE IS REDUCED SET PRINT INDICATOR
 2620 IF F(1)<FM THEN PP=1
 2630 REM IF NO REDUCTION SKIP TEST
 2640 IF PP=0 THEN GOTO 1190
 2990 REM FIND VARIANCE OF FUNCTION VALUES
 3000 S1=0:S2=0
 3020 FOR I=1 TO K:S1=S1+F(I):S2=S2+F(I)*F(I):NEXT I
 3040 SD=S2-S1*S1/K:SD=SD/K
 3090 REM FIND MAX. DIST. BETWEEN POINTS OF COMPLEX
 3100 DM=0
 3120 FOR I=1 TO K-1:FOR J=I+1 TO K
 3140 D=0
 3160 FOR L=1 TO N:D=D+(C(I,L)-C(J,L))↑2:NEXT L
 3180 D=SQR(D)
 3200 IF D>DM THEN DM=D
 3220 NEXT J:NEXT I
 3400 IF PP=0 THEN GOTO 3790
 3500 PRINT"NEW POINT AT 3500"
 3520 PRINT"MIN. VALUE="F(1)
 3540 PRINT"MIN. POINT"
 3560 FOR L=1 TO N:PRINT"X"L,C(1,L):NEXT L
 3580 PRINT""
 3600 FM=F(1):PP=0
 3790 REM TEST OF CONVERGENCE
 3800 IF SD>0.00000001 AND DM >0.0001 THEN GOTO 1190
 4000 PRINT"MINIMUM FOUND"
 4020 PRINT"MINIMUM POINT"
 4040 FOR L=1 TO N:PRINT"X"L,C(1,L):NEXT L
 4060 PRINT"FUNCTION MINIMUM="F(1)
 4080 PRINT"FUNCTION EVALUATIONS="FE
 4100 END
 5000 Z=-X(1)*X(2)*X(3)+3300
 5050 FE=FE+1
 5100 RETURN
 6000 FOR II=1 TO 2*N:EC(II)=0:NEXT II:EC=0
 6020 FOR II=1 TO M:IC(II)=0:NEXT II:IC=0
 6050 IF IM=1 THEN GOTO 7100
 6090 REM PREVIOUS LINE TAKES US TO TEST OF GI(X)<=BI
 6100 FOR II=1 TO N
 6120 IF X(II)<L(II) THEN EC(II)=1:EC=1
 6140 IF X(II)>U(II) THEN EC(N+II)=1:EC=1
 6160 NEXT II
 7100 G(1)=X(1)+2*X(2)+2*X(3)
 7110 IF G(1)>72 THEN IC(1)=1:IC=1
 8000 RETURN
 9000 DATA 0,20,0,11,0,42
READY.
```

```
COMPLEX METHOD

NO. OF CONSTRAINTS    1
NO. OF VARIABLES      3
INITIAL VALUE         20,10,10
INPUT X               7199


FIRST POINT
MIN. VALUE = 180.908875
MIN. POINT
X 1              19.2130268
X 2              9.87028714
X 3              16.4475982

NEW POINT AT 3500
MIN. VALUE = 159.33961
MIN. POINT
X 1              19.3693315
X 2              10.0923334
X 3              16.0662587

NEW POINT AT 3500
MIN. VALUE = 92.5404272
MIN. POINT
X 1              19.8689273
X 2              10.6968037
X 3              15.0915117

NEW POINT AT 3500
MIN. VALUE = 80.532506
MIN. POINT
X 1              19.9582619
X 2              10.809341
X 3              14.9232052

NEW POINT AT 3500
MIN. VALUE = 68.0381403
MIN. POINT
X 1              19.999999
X 2              10.8505043
X 3              14.8931419

..............................

NEW POINT AT 3500
MIN. VALUE = .0114955902
MIN. POINT
X 1              19.9999588
X 2              10.9999286
X 3              15.0000761

NEW POINT AT 3500
MIN. VALUE = 9.92584228E-03
MIN. POINT
X 1              19.9998837
X 2              10.9999666
X 3              15.0000876

NEW POINT AT 3500
MIN. VALUE = 8.96072388E-03
MIN. POINT
X 1              19.9999048
X 2              10.9999616
X 3              15.000083
```

```
MINIMUM FOUND
MINIMUM POINT
X 1             19.9999Ø48
X 2             1Ø.9999616
X 3             15.ØØØØ83
FUNCTION MINIMUM= 8.96Ø72388E-Ø3
FUNCTION EVALUATIONS=231
```

The Complex Method is a useful procedure which can be applied to a wide range of constrained optimisation problems. It should not however, be regarded as the panacea in this field. If the objective function is convex and the constrained region is also convex, the method should succeed, although certain peculiarities of the problem may call for some modification of the termination criteria. If the objective function is concave or the constrained region not convex it is easy to see how the method *could* fail. Indeed, in the case of a non-convex constrained region it is not even clear that the centroid of feasible points will also be feasible. Thus the moves

$$\mathbf{x}_r(\text{new}) = (\mathbf{x}_r + \mathbf{x}_0)/2$$

are not guaranteed to achieve their objective.

It is interesting to compare the situation with the conditions under which the necessary Kuhn–Tucker conditions become sufficient (see Section 5.3).

Care also needs to be taken to check that the global minimum rather than a local minimum has been found. Box suggests that making more than one run from different initial points should resolve this difficulty, and this is easy to do with the method. The random manner in which the initial complex is generated should mean that initially we generate a good coverage of the constrained region, and so will tend to converge on the global minimum. Convergence of several runs to the same result should clarify the issue.

6.3 Reference

M. J. Box, 'A new method of constrained optimisation and a comparison with other methods', *The Comp. Journal*, **8**, 42–52, 1965.

Exercises 6

1 Use the Complex Method to minimise

$$x^2 + y^2 \quad \text{if } x \geqslant 0, \quad y \geqslant 0, \quad x + y \geqslant 5.$$

2 Minimise $x^2 + 6xy - 4x - 2y$ if $x^2 + 2y \leqslant 1$, $2x - 2y \leqslant 1$.

3 Minimise $3x_1^2 + 4x_1x_2 + 5x_2^2$ if $x_1, x_2 \geqslant 0$ and $x_1 + x_2 \geqslant 4$.

4 Experiment with the program for the Complex Method by changing the values of (a) K, the number of points in the complex; line 16Ø, (b) α, the over-reflection factor; line 112Ø. Try it on the problems below and those in the text.

5 Consider the problem of minimising

$$f(x_1, x_2) = \frac{4}{x_1} + \frac{9}{x_2} + (x_1 + x_2)$$

where $x_1, x_2 \geqslant 0$, $x_1 + x_2 \leqslant S$. Consider the two cases (a) $S = 6$ (b) $S = 4$. [See also question 14 of Exercise 5.]

6 Minimise $f = -[9 - (x_1 - 3)^2]\,x_2^3/27\sqrt{3}$ where x_1 and x_2 satisfy

$$x_1 \geqslant 0, \quad 0 \leqslant x_2 \leqslant x_1/\sqrt{3}, \quad 0 \leqslant x_1 + \sqrt{3}x_2 \leqslant 6.$$

7 Minimise $x_1^4 + x_2^2$ if $x_1 \geqslant 0$, $x_2 \geqslant 0$, $x_1 x_2 \geqslant 8$.

8 Minimise $x_1^2 + x_2^2 + x_3^2$ if $x_1 + x_2 + x_3 \geqslant 3$, $x_1 x_2 x_3 \geqslant 3$. (Use (1, 2, 3) as the initial point.)

9 Minimise $(x_1 - 3)^2 + (x_2 - 4)^2$

$$\begin{aligned} \text{if} \quad 2x_1^2 + x_2^2 &\leqslant 34 \\ 2x_1 + 3x_2 &\leqslant 18 \\ x_1, x_2 &\geqslant 0. \end{aligned}$$

10 Minimise $-x_1 x_2 x_3$ for

$$\begin{aligned} x_1, x_2, x_3 &\geqslant 0 \\ 2x_1^2 + x_2^2 + 3x_3^2 &\leqslant 51. \end{aligned}$$

7

Sequential Unconstrained Optimisation

7.1 Penalty Functions

The idea underlying penalty function methods is to transform the problem of minimising

$$z = f(\mathbf{x})$$

subject to certain constraints on $\mathbf{x}$ into the problem of finding the *unconstrained* minimum of

$$Z = f(\mathbf{x}) + P(\mathbf{x}).$$

$P(\mathbf{x})$ is the penalty function. It is not unique but is required to have the property that if the constraints are violated then a high value will be given to Z so that the minimum of Z will not arise outside the constrained region.

It is convenient at this point to formulate the constrained problem in the form:

$$\text{minimise} \quad z = f(\mathbf{x}) \tag{7.1}$$

$$\text{subject to} \quad c_j(\mathbf{x}) \geqslant 0; \quad j = 1, 2, \ldots, m. \tag{7.2}$$

N.B. a 'less than or equal to' constraint $h(\mathbf{x}) \leqslant 0$ can always be written $-h(\mathbf{x}) \geqslant 0$ so there is no loss of generality.

A useful form for $P(\mathbf{x})$ is then

$$P(\mathbf{x}) = r \sum_{j=1}^{m} \frac{1}{c_j(\mathbf{x})}. \tag{7.3}$$

where r is *positive*. The function $Z = \phi(\mathbf{x}, r)$ then takes the form

$$Z = \phi(\mathbf{x}, r) = f(\mathbf{x}) + r \sum_{j=1}^{m} \frac{1}{c_j(\mathbf{x})} \tag{7.4}$$

Now as $\mathbf{x}$ takes on feasible values, i.e values for which $c_j(\mathbf{x}) \geqslant 0$, Z takes on values which are greater than the corresponding values of $f(\mathbf{x})$ (the true objective function for our problem), although the difference may be reduced by allowing r to become very small. However, if $\mathbf{x}$ takes on values, which though feasible, are close to the boundary of the constrained region, so that at least one of the $c_j(\mathbf{x})$ is near to zero, $P(\mathbf{x})$ and hence Z will become very large. Thus the effect of $P(\mathbf{x})$ is to create a steep sided ridge along each of the constraint boundaries. Hence if we start with a feasible point and try to find the unconstrained minimum of $\phi(\mathbf{x}, r)$ it will certainly lie within the feasible region of our constrained problem. By giving r a suitably small value, so that the effect of $P(\mathbf{x})$ is small at the minimum point, we may be able to make this *unconstrained* minimum point for $\phi(\mathbf{x}, r)$ coincide with the *constrained* minimum of $f(\mathbf{x})$.

Let us consider a very simple example, but one which allows us to appreciate 'what is going on'.

Example 1

Use the penalty function given by equation 7.4 to minimise

$$f(x) = x$$

where $x \geqslant 2$, i.e. $x - 2 \geqslant 0$. The minimum value is clearly 2, when $x = 2$. How does the penalty function method find the solution? Consider the function

$$\phi(x, r) = x + \frac{r}{x - 2}.$$

Figure 7.1 shows the graph of $\phi(x, r)$ and the position of its minimum point for various values of r ($=1, 0{\cdot}25, 0{\cdot}01$).

The constrained region is to the right of the vertical line $x = 2$. We can see that the sequence of points Q_1, Q_2, Q_3 is approaching the constrained minimum point Q. Indeed it is easy to find the minimum of $\phi(x, r)$ by the methods of Chapter 1.

$$\frac{d\phi}{dx} = 1 - \frac{r}{(x - 2)^2}$$

Thus when

$$d\phi/dx = 0, \quad (x - 2)^2 = r$$

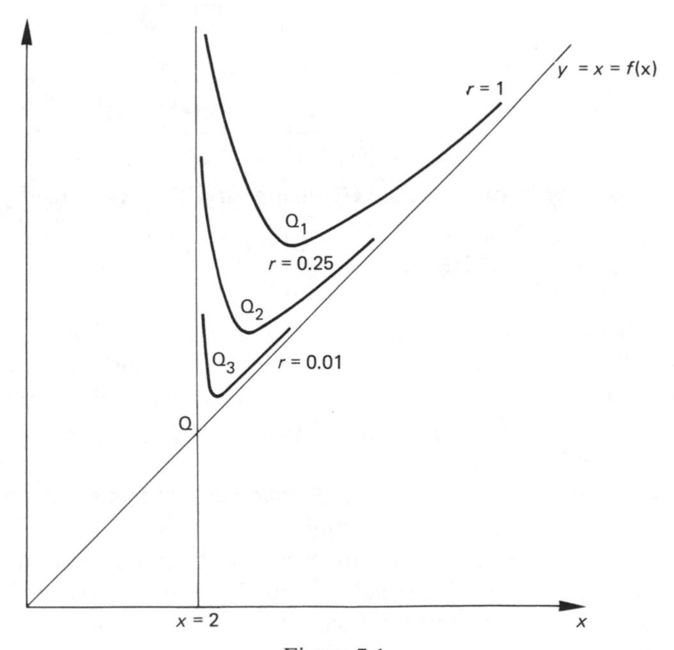

Figure 7.1

so that

$$x = 2 \pm \sqrt{r}.$$

$$\frac{d^2\phi}{dx^2} = \frac{2r}{(x-2)^3}$$

and the minimum arises when $x = 2 + \sqrt{r}$ (within the constrained region).

Thus $\phi(x, r)$ has a minimum of $2 + 2\sqrt{r}$ when $x = 2 + \sqrt{r}$. Thus Q_1 is the point (3, 4), Q_2 (2·5, 3), Q_3 (2·1, 2·2). Clearly as $r \to 0$ the unconstrained minimum of $\phi(x, r)$ approaches the value 2 and the location of the minimum point, the value $x = 2$.

In general it will not be possible to locate the position of the minimum of $\phi(x, r)$ analytically as a simple function of r, and it will be necessary to resort to numerical techniques for its calculation.

It should be noted that if the objective function $f(\mathbf{x})$ is convex, and the $c_j(\mathbf{x})$ are concave, then $\phi(\mathbf{x}, r)$ as given by equation 7.4 is also a convex function over the constrained region, which is itself a convex region. Thus $\phi(\mathbf{x}, r)$ has a unique minimum for a given value of r.

We can see that the feasible region is convex, for if $\mathbf{x}_1$ and $\mathbf{x}_2$ are points which belong to the feasible region, i.e. $c_j(\mathbf{x}_1) \geqslant 0$ and $c_j(\mathbf{x}_2) \geqslant 0$ for $j = 1, 2, \ldots, m$, then if $0 < \theta < 1$,

$$c_j(\theta\mathbf{x}_2 + (1-\theta)\mathbf{x}_1) \geqslant \theta c_j(\mathbf{x}_2) + (1-\theta)c_j(\mathbf{x}_1) \quad [\text{since } c_j(\mathbf{x}) \text{ is concave}]$$
$$\geqslant 0.$$

Thus $\mathbf{x}_2 + (1-\theta)\mathbf{x}_1$ for $0 < \theta < 1$ is also feasible. [Compare Example 2 of Section 5.3.]

In addition $1/c_j(\mathbf{x})$ is convex for all $\mathbf{x}$ for which $c_j(\mathbf{x}) \geqslant 0$. For if $h(\mathbf{x}) = 1/c_j(\mathbf{x})$.

$$\nabla h(\mathbf{x}) = \frac{-\nabla c(\mathbf{x})}{[c_j(\mathbf{x})]^2}.$$

Thus the Hessian matrix of $h(\mathbf{x})$ is given by

$$H(\mathbf{x}) = -\frac{\mathbf{C}(\mathbf{x})}{[c_j(\mathbf{x})]^2} + \frac{2\nabla c(\mathbf{x})\,\nabla c(\mathbf{x})^{\mathrm{T}}}{[c_j(\mathbf{x})]^3}$$

where $\mathbf{C}(\mathbf{x})_{ik} = \partial^2 c_j(\mathbf{x})/\partial x_i\,\partial x_k$ is the Hessian matrix of $c_j(\mathbf{x})$. Thus if $\mathbf{p}$ is any vector

$$\mathbf{p}^{\mathrm{T}}\,\mathbf{H}(\mathbf{x})\,\mathbf{p} = -\frac{\mathbf{p}^{\mathrm{T}}\,\mathbf{C}(\mathbf{x})\,\mathbf{p}}{[c_j(\mathbf{x})]^2} + \frac{2[\mathbf{p}^{\mathrm{T}}\,\nabla c(\mathbf{x})]^2}{[c_j(\mathbf{x})]^3}$$

and this is always positive, since $\mathbf{C}(\mathbf{x})$ is negative definite because $c_j(\mathbf{x})$ is concave, and of course $c_j(\mathbf{x}) \geqslant 0$. Thus $\mathbf{H}(\mathbf{x})$ is positive definite so that $1/c_j(\mathbf{x})$ is convex over the region. (Compare question 11 of Exercises 5.) It follows by the result given in Example 1 of Section 5.3 that, since r is positive, $P(\mathbf{x})$ (as given by equation 7.3) and $\phi(\mathbf{x}, r)$ (as given by equation 7.4) are also convex.

It is possible to generalise the result of Example 1 of this section to the general constrained problem (equations 7.1 and 7.2).

Suppose $\mathbf{x}_1^*, \mathbf{x}_2^*, \ldots, \mathbf{x}_k^*$ are the minimum points of $\phi(\mathbf{x}, r_k)$ for the decreasing sequence of values $r_1, r_2, \ldots, r_k \ldots$ which tend to zero. Then the sequence of points $\mathbf{x}_1^*, \mathbf{x}_2^*, \ldots, \mathbf{x}_k^* \ldots$. converges to the optimal solution of the constrained problem (equations 7.1 and 7.2) as $r_k \to 0$.

Thus

$$\lim_{r_k \to 0} \mathbf{x}_k^* = \mathbf{x}^* \tag{7.5}$$

and

$$\lim_{r_k \to 0} [\text{Min } \phi(\mathbf{x}, r_k)] = f(\mathbf{x}^*) \tag{7.6}$$

where $\mathbf{x}^*$ is the constrained minimum point of $f(\mathbf{x})$.

We can prove this result as follows. Since $f(\mathbf{x})$ is continuous and $f(\mathbf{x}^*) \leqslant f(\mathbf{x})$ for all feasible points, given any positive ε however small we can find a feasible point $\mathbf{x}'$ such that

$$f(\mathbf{x}') < f(\mathbf{x}^*) + \varepsilon/2. \tag{7.7}$$

Since r_k is a decreasing sequence tending to zero we can find a value of k so that for $k \geqslant K$

$$r_k \leqslant \left\{ \frac{\varepsilon}{2m} \min_j \left[\frac{1}{c_j(\mathbf{x}')} \right] \right\}. \tag{7.8}$$

Since $P(\mathbf{x})$ is positive, from the definition of $\phi(\mathbf{x}, r)$ we have

$$f(\mathbf{x}^*) \leqslant \min \phi(\mathbf{x}, r_k) = \phi(\mathbf{x}_k^*, r_k) \tag{7.9}$$

where $\mathbf{x}_k^*$ is the unconstrained minimum point of $\phi(\mathbf{x}, r_k)$.

In addition for $k > K$, $r_k < r_K$ and

$$\phi(\mathbf{x}_k^*, r_k) \leqslant \phi(\mathbf{x}_K^*, r_k) \tag{7.10}$$

This follows since $\mathbf{x}_k^*$ minimises $\phi(\mathbf{x}, r_k)$ and any other value for $\mathbf{x}$, in particular the value $\mathbf{x}_K^*$, will give a value at least as large as $\phi(\mathbf{x}_k^*, r_k)$.

It is also true that

$$\begin{aligned} \phi(\mathbf{x}_K^*, r_K) &= f(\mathbf{x}_K^*) + r_K \sum_{j=1}^{m} \frac{1}{c_j(\mathbf{x}_K^*)} \\ &> f(\mathbf{x}_K^*) + r_k \sum_{j=1}^{m} \frac{1}{c_j(\mathbf{x}_K^*)} \end{aligned}$$

since $r_k < r_K$.

$$\therefore \quad \phi(\mathbf{x}_K^*, r_K) > \phi(\mathbf{x}_K^*, r_k).$$

Thus

$$f(\mathbf{x}^*) \leqslant \phi(\mathbf{x}_k^*, r_k) \leqslant \phi(\mathbf{x}_K^*, r_k) < \phi(\mathbf{x}_K^*, r_K). \tag{7.11}$$

But since $\mathbf{x}_K^*$ minimises $\phi(\mathbf{x}, r_K)$

$$\phi(\mathbf{x}_K^*, r_K) \leqslant \phi(\mathbf{x}', r_K) = f(\mathbf{x}') + r_K \sum_{j=1}^{m} \frac{1}{c_j(\mathbf{x}')}. \tag{7.12}$$

Thus from equations 7.11 and 7.12

$$f(\mathbf{x}^*) \leqslant \phi(\mathbf{x}_k^*, r_k) \leqslant f(\mathbf{x}') + r_K \sum_{j=1}^{m} \frac{1}{c_j(\mathbf{x}')} \tag{7.13}$$

$$\leqslant f(x') + \frac{\varepsilon}{2} \quad \text{by equation 7.8} \tag{7.14}$$

Then from equation 7.7 we obtain

$$f(\mathbf{x}^*) \leqslant \phi(\mathbf{x}_k^*, r_k) < f(\mathbf{x}^*) + \frac{\varepsilon}{2} + \frac{\varepsilon}{2}$$

so that

$$\phi(\mathbf{x}_k^*, r_k) - f(\mathbf{x}^*) < \varepsilon. \tag{7.15}$$

Thus although ε can be chosen arbitrarily small we can always find values for k so that

$$f(\mathbf{x}^*) < \phi(\mathbf{x}_k^*, r_k) < f(\mathbf{x}^*) + \varepsilon.$$

Thus as $k \to \infty$ $(r_k \to 0)$

$$\operatorname*{Lim}_{r_k \to 0} \phi(\mathbf{x}_k^*, r_k) = f(\mathbf{x}^*). \tag{7.16}$$

It follows from the above proof that as $r_k \to 0$

$$f(\mathbf{x}_k^*) \to f(\mathbf{x}^*) \quad \text{and} \quad r_k \sum_{j=1}^{m} \frac{1}{c_j(\mathbf{x}_k^*)} \to 0. \tag{7.17}$$

It can also be shown although the proof is left as an exercise that $f(\mathbf{x}_1^*)$, $f(\mathbf{x}_2^*)$, ..., $f(\mathbf{x}_k^*)$ also form a decreasing sequence so that

$$f(\mathbf{x}_{k+1}^*) < f(\mathbf{x}_k^*). \tag{7.18}$$

Of course if $f(\mathbf{x})$ is convex and the $c_j(\mathbf{x})$ are concave the constrained minimum of $f(\mathbf{x})$ is unique. (Compare with the results of Section 5.3.)

Example 2

As a second example, where once again an analytical solution is possible, consider the following problem.

Minimise

$$f(x_1, x_2) = \tfrac{1}{3}(x_1 + 1)^3 + x_2$$

where $x_1 - 1 \geqslant 0$, $x_2 \geqslant 0$. In line with equation 7.4

$$\phi(\mathbf{x}, r) = \tfrac{1}{3}(x_1 + 1)^3 + x_2 + r\left(\frac{1}{x_1 - 1} + \frac{1}{x_2}\right).$$

The necessary conditions for the minimum of ϕ give

$$(x_1 + 1)^2 - \frac{r}{(x_1 - 1)^2} = 0,$$

$$1 - \frac{r}{x_2^2} = 0,$$

with solutions

$$x_1(r) = (1 + \sqrt{r}), \quad x_2(r) = \sqrt{r}.$$

The minimum value of $\phi(\mathbf{x}, r)$ is then

$$\phi^*(r) = \left\{ \tfrac{1}{3}[(1 + \sqrt{r})^{1/2} + 1]^3 + \sqrt{r} + r\left[\frac{1}{\sqrt{r}} + \frac{1}{(1 + \sqrt{r})^{1/2} - 1}\right]\right\}$$

$$= \left\{ \tfrac{1}{3}[(1 + \sqrt{r})^{1/2} + 1]^3 + \sqrt{r} + r\left[\frac{1}{\sqrt{r}} + \frac{(1 + \sqrt{r})^{1/2} + 1}{\sqrt{r}}\right]\right\}$$

$$= \{\tfrac{1}{3}[(1 + \sqrt{r})^{1/2} + 1]^3 + \sqrt{r} + \sqrt{r}[1 + 1 + (1 + \sqrt{r})^{1/2}]\}$$

Thus we see that as $r \to 0$

$$x_1(r) \to 1, \quad x_2(r) \to 0$$

and

$$\phi^*(r) \to f(1, 0) = \tfrac{8}{3}$$

the results (equations 7.17) being apparent in this particular case.

7.2 The SUMT Method of Fiacco and McCormick

The results of the previous section show that we can solve the constrained minimisation problem, minimise $f(\mathbf{x})$ subject to $c_j(\mathbf{x}) \geqslant 0$, by solving the sequence of unconstrained problems,

$$\text{minimise} \quad \phi(\mathbf{x}, r) = f(\mathbf{x}) + r \sum_{j=1}^{m} \frac{1}{c_j(\mathbf{x})}$$

for a sequence of r values which tend to zero.

This sequential unconstrained minimisation technique (SUMT) was first suggested by Carroll in 1961. His ideas were very thoroughly developed and investigated by Fiacco and McCormick, who not only considered the theory and convergence properties of the method but also developed a practical system for its implementation.

It will seldom be possible to use the method as was done in the two examples of the previous section. It will be rare indeed to be able to find the optimal point of $\phi(\mathbf{x}, r)$ in the form of a function of r, $\mathbf{x}^*(r)$, whose limit as $r \to 0$ can be investigated.

Thus in order to be able to exploit the method in a practical manner, we have to turn the theoretical convergence property of the previous section into a computational reality. In theory there is no problem. Given $f(\mathbf{x})$ and the constraint functions $c_j(\mathbf{x})$ ($\geqslant 0$) we have to choose an initial value for r $(=r_0)$ (is there a problem there?) to form the function $\phi(\mathbf{x}, r_0)$. This must be minimised and this minimisation can be treated as an unconstrained problem. The Davidon–Fletcher–Powell technique of Chapter 4 should be able to cope with this. Having found the minimum of $\phi(\mathbf{x}, r_0)$ we must reduce the value of r. A simple and effective way to do this is to find $r_1 = r_0/c$ where c is a constant greater than 1. In the program given c is chosen to be 10 but this is arbitrary. Values of 12 and 16 etc. will also be successful. We must then minimise $\phi(\mathbf{x}, r_1)$ again using the Davidon–Fletcher–Powell technique. Thus we shall indeed develop an iterative procedure. At stage k we minimise $\phi(\mathbf{x}, r_k)$ with minimum point $\mathbf{x}_k^*$. This can be used, and this is an important computational point, as the first point in the iterative procedure to minimise $\phi(\mathbf{x}, r_{k+1})$ where $r_{k+1} = r_k/c$. Thus it is clear that the r_k form a decreasing sequence tending to zero, and hopefully the sequence of minimum points will converge to the solution of the constrained problem.

The flow chart for the SUMT method follows. There are still however one or two detailed points to settle.

Flow Chart for SUMT

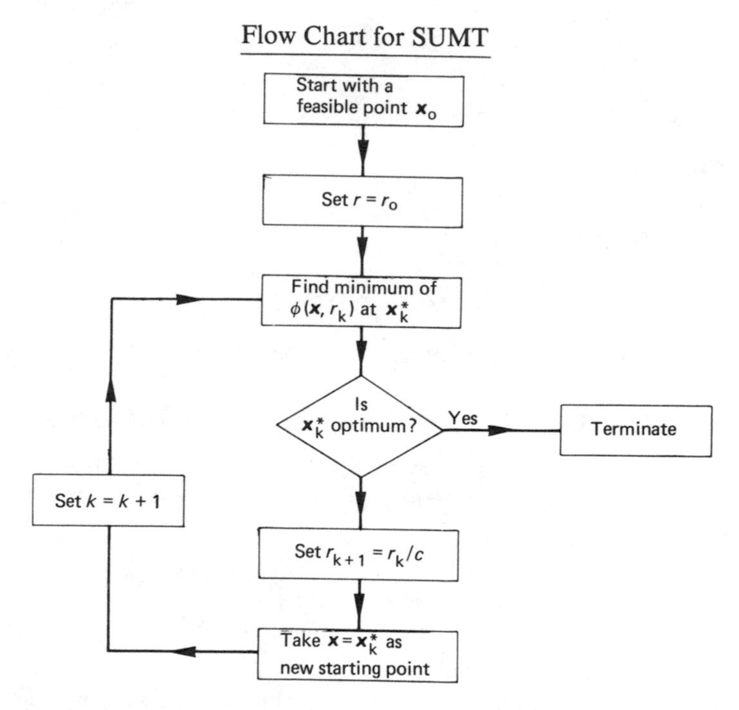

It is assumed that we have a feasible point at the outset. It is important that in the subsequent computations the points always remain within the feasible region. The Davidon–Fletcher–Powell minimisation procedure is a gradient based method which uses cubic interpolation in its linear searches. Now as $\mathbf{x}$ approaches a constraint from within the feasible region, $\phi(\mathbf{x}, r) \rightarrow \infty$ and as $\mathbf{x}$ approaches a constraint from outside the feasible region, $\phi(\mathbf{x}, r) \rightarrow -\infty$. Thus if the search is made along a line joining two points, one inside and one outside the contrained region, the cubic interpolation will break down since the function has a discontinuity along the line. The minimum will be found outside the region. The method will never be able to re-enter the constrained region and so will fail. These points will need to be considered when using the D.F.P. procedure in the context of this problem.

The initial value to give to r can be important in reducing the number of iterations to minimise $\phi(\mathbf{x}, r)$. It might appear that if r is chosen to be very small at the outset, so that $\phi(\mathbf{x}, r)$ is close to $f(\mathbf{x})$ the method should converge more quickly. However, such a choice can cause serious computational problems. We can see from Fig. 7.1 that for small r the function $\phi(\mathbf{x}, r)$ will change rapidly in the vicinity of its minimum. This rapid change in the function can cause difficulties for a gradient based technique. Of course too large a value of r may mean that the penalty function $P(\mathbf{x})$ in equation 7.4 becomes too dominant. What is required at the outset is a 'reasonable' value.

In many problems the value $r_0 = 1$ is sensible. A more reasoned approach is to realise that if our starting point $\mathbf{x}$ is to be near the minimum of

$$\begin{aligned}\phi(\mathbf{x}, r) &= f(\mathbf{x}) + r \sum_{j=1}^{m} \frac{1}{c_j(\mathbf{x})}\\ &= f(\mathbf{x}) + rP(\mathbf{x})\end{aligned}$$

then the gradient of $\phi(\mathbf{x}, r)$ should be small.

$$\nabla\phi(\mathbf{x}, r) = \nabla f(\mathbf{x}) + r\nabla P(\mathbf{x}). \tag{7.19}$$

The squared magnitude of this vector is

$$\nabla f(\mathbf{x})^{\mathrm{T}}\,\nabla f(\mathbf{x}) + 2r\nabla f(\mathbf{x})^{\mathrm{T}}\,\nabla P(\mathbf{x}) + r^2\,\nabla P(\mathbf{x})^{\mathrm{T}}\,\nabla P(\mathbf{x}) \tag{7.20}$$

and this is a minimum when

$$r = \frac{-\nabla f(\mathbf{x})^{\mathrm{T}}\,\nabla P(\mathbf{x})}{\nabla P(\mathbf{x})^{\mathrm{T}}\,\nabla P(\mathbf{x})}. \tag{7.21}$$

This initial value for r, as suggested by Fiacco and McCormick, appears to give good results in general. The method of reducing r is simple: $r_{k+1} = r_k/c$ where $c = 10$.

The method used to minimise $\phi(\mathbf{x}, r_{k+1})$ is the Davidon–Fletcher–Powell method of Chapter 4. The optimal point of $\phi(\mathbf{x}, r_k)$ is used as the starting value and this appears to be very efficient. The program follows that given in Chapter 4, but care needs to be taken that in doing the linear searches we do not step outside the constrained region. A crude but effective way of doing this is as follows. We have a point $\mathbf{p}$ and a search direction $\mathbf{d} = -\mathbf{Hg}$ (see equation 4.34). A further point $\mathbf{q} = \mathbf{p} + \lambda\mathbf{d}$ is needed in order to set up the cubic interpolation. We start with $\lambda = 2$ (twice the Newton step length) and test if $\mathbf{q}$ is feasible. We thus test $c_j(\mathbf{q})$ to see that it is positive for all j. If so we retain λ, but if a constraint is violated we replace λ by λ/a, form a new point $\mathbf{q}$ and test again. Eventually we find a feasible $\mathbf{q}$ and we can then proceed with the interpolation. The choice of a is not clear. $a = 2$ was successful. By choosing $a = 1{\cdot}05$, our step length becomes close to the distance to the nearest constraint boundary and so is 'safe' for the interpolation process. These steps are carried out at lines 63Ø–75Ø of the program.

The importance of not allowing points to step outside the constrained region during the minimisation process cannot be over-emphasised. To this end further precautions have been taken at lines 11ØØ–112Ø to ensure that we find the minimum by interpolation between the two trial points. Although the modification to $\mathbf{H}$ at 111Ø is semi-heuristic it does appear to be successful.

The minimisation of $\phi(\mathbf{x}, r)$ is carried out until two successive function values F_1 and F_2 are found such that $|(F_1 - F_2)/F_1| < 0{\cdot}000\,001$. This condition could of course be modified (line 157Ø). In line with equation 7.17 the program terminates when (line 16ØØ)

$$r \sum_{j=1}^{m} \frac{1}{c_j(x_k^*)} < 0{\cdot}000\,001.$$

This will give 5 decimal place accuracy for the minimum of $f(\mathbf{x})$. Of course the accuracy here could be varied. A simpler termination criterion which was also successful was to stop when r_k took on a value less than 10^{-12}.

A program listing follows. The subroutines as written are appropriate for the solution of the problem:

$$\text{minimise} \quad f(\mathbf{x}) = (x_1 - 1)(x_1 - 2)(x_1 - 3) + x_3$$

$$\text{subject to} \quad x_1, x_2, x_3 \geqslant 0$$

$$x_3^2 - x_1^2 - x_2^2 \geqslant 0, \quad x_1^2 + x_2^2 + x_3^2 - 4 \geqslant 0, \quad x_3 \leqslant 5,$$

so that

$$\phi(\mathbf{x}, r) = f(\mathbf{x}) + r\left(\frac{1}{x_3^2 - x_1^2 - x_2^2} + \frac{1}{x_1^2 + x_2^2 + x_3^2 - 4} + \frac{1}{5 - x_3} + \frac{1}{x_1} + \frac{1}{x_2} + \frac{1}{x_3}\right).$$

We thus have a problem in 3 variables with 6 constraints. The objective function is not convex. The constraint region is not convex but the method is none the less successful. With starting point (0·1, 2, 2·1) the solution was found after 48 iterations. The true minimum point is at $(0, \sqrt{2}, \sqrt{2})$ with function value $-6 + \sqrt{2}$. The first and last page of the output have been given. The value of using the optimal point of the previous r value as the starting point for the next r value can be seen by the small number of iterations required to find the later minima.

```
READY.

 20 PRINT"      FIACCO&MACORMICK"
 40 REM Z=F(X1,X2..XN) AT 5ØØØ
 6Ø REM GRADIENT G(1),G(2)...G(N) AT 6ØØØ
 8Ø REM CONSTRAINTS C(1),C(2),..C(M) AT 8ØØØ
 1ØØ PRINT"NO. OF VARIABLES":INPUT N
 12Ø PRINT"NO. OF CONSTRAINTS ":INPUT M
 14Ø DIM X,P,Y,U,G,CG,D,V,R(N)
 15Ø DIM H(N,N)
 16Ø DIM C(M),IC(M)
 18Ø PRINT"INITIAL POINT X1,X2,..XN"
 19Ø FOR I=1 TO N:INPUT X(I):NEXT I
 2ØØ REM TEST CONSTRAINTS
 2Ø5 REM IC(J)=Ø;CONSTRAINT J OK:IC(J)=1;CONSTRAINT J VIOLATED
 21Ø S=Ø
 22Ø FOR II=1 TO M:GOSUB 8ØØØ
 23Ø IF C(II)<Ø THEN S=S+1:IC(II)=1
 24Ø NEXT II
 25Ø IF S>Ø THEN PRINT"FIRST POINT NOT FEASIBLE":STOP
 27Ø REM FIND INITIAL VALUE OF R
 29Ø T=Ø:B=Ø:R=Ø
 3ØØ GOSUB 6ØØØ
```

```
310 FOR I=1 TO N
320 T=T-G(I)*CG(I):B=B+CG(I)*CG(I):NEXT I
350 R=T/B
360 IF R<0 THEN R=1
410 PRINT"R="R
420 REM SET H MATRIX TO UNIT MATRIX AT START OF NEW MINIMISATION
430 FOR I=1 TO N:FOR J=1 TO N
440 H(I,J)=0:NEXT J
450 H(I,I)=1:NEXT I
460 REM INTERMEDIATE OUTPUT
480 PRINT"         CURRENT VALUES"
500 FOR I=1 TO N:P(I)=X(I):Y(I)=X(I):PRINT"X";I,X(I):NEXT I
510 FOR II=1 TO M:GOSUB 8000:NEXT II:GOSUB 5000
520 PRINT"ITERATION"CC"VALUE"Z
530 FP=Z:GOSUB 6000:G1=G0:FF=Z
540 REM STORE GRADIENT IN U AND SET SEARCH DIRECTION
550 FOR I=1 TO N
560 U(I)=G(I):D(I)=0
570 FOR J=1 TO N
580 D(I)=D(I)-H(I,J)*G(J)
590 NEXT J:NEXT I
595 REM FIND GRADIENT AT FIRST POINT FOR LINEAR SEARCH
600 GP=0
610 FOR I=1 TO N:GP=GP+G(I)*D(I):NEXT I
620 IF GP>0 THEN PRINT"UPHILL AT 620"
625 REM FIND VALUE FOR LAMDA SO THAT NO CONSTRAINT IS VIOLATED
630 L=2
640 FOR I=1 TO N:X(I)=P(I)+L*D(I):NEXT I
650 S=0
660 FOR II=1 TO M
670 IC(II)=0:GOSUB 8000
680 IF C(II)>=0 THEN GOTO 730
690 IC(II)=1:S=S+1
700 L=L/1.05
710 FOR I=1 TO N:X(I)=P(I)+L*D(I):NEXT I
720 GOTO 670
730 NEXT II
750 IF S>0 THEN GOTO 650
1000 REM FIND NEXT POINT Q
1010 HH=L
1020 FOR I=1 TO N
1030 Q(I)=P(I)+HH*D(I):X(I)=Q(I)
1040 NEXT I
1050 FOR II=1 TO M:GOSUB 8000:NEXT II:GOSUB 5000:FQ=Z
1060 GOSUB 6000:G2=G0
1080 GQ=0
1090 FOR I=1 TO N:GQ=GQ+G(I)*D(I):NEXT I
1095 REM IF NO MIN. BETWEEN P&Q REPLACE P BY Q
1096 REM MODIFY H AND FIND NEW DIRECTION
1100 IF GQ<0 AND FQ<FP THEN GOTO 1110
1105 GOTO 1125
1110 FOR I=1 TO N:FOR J=1 TO N:H(I,J)=H(I,J)-D(I)*D(J)/GP:NEXT J
1115 P(I)=Q(I):X(I)=P(I):Y(I)=X(I):NEXT I
1120 FF=Z:FP=Z:G1=G0:GOTO 540
1125 REM CUBIC INTERPOLATION FOLLOWS
1130 ZZ=3*(FP-FQ)/HH:ZZ=ZZ+GP+GQ
1140 WW=ZZ*ZZ-GP*GQ:IF WW<0 THEN WW=0
1150 W=SQR(WW)
1160 DD=HH*(1-(GQ+W-ZZ)/(GQ-GP+2*W))
1170 FOR I=1 TO N:X(I)=P(I)+DD*D(I):NEXT I
1180 FOR II=1 TO M:GOSUB 8000:NEXT II:GOSUB 5000:FR=Z
1195 REM FIND GRADIENT AT NEW POINT
1200 GR=0
1210 FOR I=1 TO N:GR=GR+G(I)*D(I):NEXT I
1215 REM REPEAT INTERPOLATION ON NEXT INTERVAL
```

```
1216 REM (1260 OR 1290) OR PROCEED
1220 IF Z<=FP AND Z<=FQ THEN GOTO 1400
1230 IF GR>0 THEN GOTO 1290
1260 HH=HH-DD
1270 FOR I=1 TO N:P(I)=X(I):NEXT I
1280 FP=Z:GP=GR:G1=G0:GOTO 1130
1290 HH=DD
1300 FOR I=1 TO N:Q(I)=X(I):NEXT I
1310 FQ=Z:GQ=GR:G2=G0:GOTO 1130
1350 REM UPDATE THE H MATRIX
1400 KK=0:WK=0:DK=0
1410 FOR I=1 TO N
1420 U(I)=G(I)-U(I):V(I)=X(I)-Y(I)
1430 NEXT I
1440 FOR I=1 TO N:M(I)=0
1450 FOR J=1 TO N
1460 M(I)=M(I)+H(I,J)*U(J)
1470 NEXT J
1480 KK=KK+M(I)*U(I):WK=WK+V(I)*U(I)
1500 NEXT I
1505 IF KK=0 OR WK=0 THEN GOTO 1560
1510 FOR I=1 TO N
1520 FOR J=1 TO N
1530 H(I,J)=H(I,J)-M(I)*M(J)/KK+V(I)*V(J)/WK
1540 NEXT J
1550 NEXT I
1560 CC=CC+1
1565 REM TEST FOR MINIMUM OF PHI(X,R)
1570 IF ABS((FF-Z)/FF)<0.000001 THEN GOTO 1600
1575 REM IF NOT CONVERGED START NEW LINEAR SEARCH FROM LATEST POINT
1580 FF=Z:GOTO 500
1590 REM TEST FOR FINAL CONVERGENCE;
1595 REM IF NOT REDUCE R AND FORM NEW PHI(X,R)
1600 IF R*Z2<0.000001 THEN GOTO 1800
1610 R=R/10
1620 GOTO 410
1800 PRINT"FINAL SOLUTION"
1820 FOR I=1 TO N
1830 PRINT"X"I"="X(I)
1840 NEXT I
1850 PRINT"F(X)="Z1
2000 END
5000 REM F(X) IS FOUND AS Z1;P(X) AS Z2
5010 Z1=(X(1)-1)*(X(1)-2)*(X(1)-3)+X(3)
5100 Z2=0
5110 FOR JJ=1 TO M:Z2=Z2+1/C(JJ):NEXT JJ
5200 Z=Z1+R*Z2
5500 RETURN
6000 REM GRADIENT OF F(X) IS G(1)..G(N);
6005 REM GRADIENT OF P(X) IS CG(1)..CG(N)
6010 REM THEN THEY ARE COMBINED AS G(1)..G(N).
6050 KA=X(1)-1:KB=X(1)-2:KC=X(1)-3
6100 G(1)=KA*KB+KB*KC+KC*KA
6150 CG(1)=-(-2*X(1)/(C(1)*C(1))+2*X(1)/(C(2)*C(2))+1/(C(4)*C(4)))
6190 G(1)=G(1)+R*CG(1)
6200 G(2)=0
6250 CG(2)=-(-2*X(2)/(C(1)*C(1))+2*X(2)/(C(2)*C(2))+1/(C(5)*C(5)))
6290 G(2)=G(2)+R*CG(2)
6300 G(3)=1
6350 CG(3)=-(2*X(3)/(C(1)*C(1))+2*X(3)/(C(2)*C(2))-1/(C(3)*C(3)))
6360 CG(3)=CG(3)-1/(C(6)*C(6))
6390 G(3)=G(3)+R*CG(3)
6900 G0=0
6910 FOR JJ=1 TO N:G0=G0+G(JJ)*G(JJ):NEXT JJ
6920 G0=SQR(G0)
```

```
 699Ø RETURN
 8ØØØ REM CONSTRAINTS FOUND AS C(1),C(2)...C(M)
 8ØØ5 ON II GOTO 8Ø1Ø,8Ø2Ø,8Ø3Ø,8Ø4Ø,8Ø5Ø,8Ø6Ø
 8Ø1Ø C(1)=X(3)*X(3)-X(1)*X(1)-X(2)*X(2):GOTO 85ØØ
 8Ø2Ø C(2)=X(1)*X(1)+X(2)*X(2)+X(3)*X(3)-4:GOTO 85ØØ
 8Ø3Ø C(3)=5-X(3):GOTO 85ØØ
 8Ø4Ø C(4)=X(1):GOTO 85ØØ
 8Ø5Ø C(5)=X(2):GOTO 85ØØ
 8Ø6Ø C(6)=X(3):GOTO 85ØØ
 85ØØ RETURN
READY.
```

```
      FIACCO&MACORMICK
 NO. OF VARIABLES             3
 NO. OF CONSTRAINTS           6
 INITIAL POINT X1,X2,..XN     Ø.1, 2.Ø, 2.1
 R= .Ø9Ø161877
        CURRENT VALUES
 X 1            .1
 X 2            2
 X 3            2.1
 ITERATION Ø VALUE-1.59247246
 X 1            .Ø8Ø6Ø53572
 X 2            1.95362832
 X 3            2.12924847
 ITERATION 1 VALUE-1.6365Ø376
 X 1            .Ø8Ø6144181
 X 2            1.28737685
 X 3            1.91561499
 ITERATION 2 VALUE-1.85875819
 X 1            .Ø8Ø6Ø7ØØ93
 X 2            1.54877Ø57
 X 3            1.76992234
 ITERATION 3 VALUE-1.94368135
 X 1            .Ø8Ø623Ø48
 X 2            1.433Ø8753
 X 3            1.65843191
 ITERATION 4 VALUE-1.98875162
 X 1            .Ø8Ø82119Ø6
 X 2            1.41538473
 X 3            1.671Ø4433
 ITERATION 5 VALUE-1.99Ø6691
 X 1            .Ø8Ø8324961
 X 2            1.41536793
 X 3            1.6725885
 ITERATION 6 VALUE-1.99Ø678Ø5
 X 1            .Ø955Ø73433
 X 2            1.41863623
 X 3            1.6691519
 ITERATION 7 VALUE-2.Ø1588Ø76
 R= 9.Ø161877E-Ø3
        CURRENT VALUES
 X 1            .Ø955Ø77823
 X 2            1.4185Ø388
 X 3            1.66923548
 ITERATION 8 VALUE-3.2Ø222241
 X 1            .Ø36254Ø564
 X 2            1.4185Ø386
 X 3            1.66323888
 ITERATION 9 VALUE-3.659Ø9428
 X 1            .Ø361856916
 X 2            1.41875962
 X 3            1.5Ø286992
```

```
ITERATION 1Ø VALUE-3.77286321
X 1            .Ø361589543
X 2            1.4Ø956641
X 3            1.494Ø331
ITERATION 11 VALUE-3.773782Ø3
X 1            .Ø29Ø899Ø43
X 2            1.4Ø983197
X 3            1.49397824
ITERATION 12 VALUE-3.78821358

....................................

X 1            1.Ø1423734E-Ø5
X 2            1.414210Ø79
X 3            1.41429273
ITERATION 39 VALUE-4.58549875
X 1            1.Ø1424578E-Ø5
X 2            1.41421117
X 3            1.414245Ø4
ITERATION 4Ø VALUE-4.58553413
R= 9.Ø161877E-11
       CURRENT VALUES
X 1            1.Ø1424637E-Ø5
X 2            1.41421696
X 3            1.414240Ø98
ITERATION 41 VALUE-4.5856362
X 1            3.751150Ø52E-Ø6
X 2            1.41421695
X 3            1.414240Ø41
ITERATION 42 VALUE-4.58569188
X 1            3.751260Ø12E-Ø6
X 2            1.41421657
X 3            1.41422536
ITERATION 43 VALUE-4.58570Ø356
R= 9.Ø161877E-12
       CURRENT VALUES
X 1            3.75128267E-Ø6
X 2            1.41421155
X 3            1.414220Ø53
ITERATION 44 VALUE-4.5857348
X 1            1.39583139E-Ø6
X 2            1.41421157
X 3            1.414220Ø34
ITERATION 45 VALUE-4.58575681
R= 9.Ø161877E-13
       CURRENT VALUES
X 1            1.39596479E-Ø6
X 2            1.41421198
X 3            1.41421686
ITERATION 46 VALUE-4.58576689
X 1            4.82Ø31713E-Ø7
X 2            1.41421199
X 3            1.41421678
ITERATION 47 VALUE-4.58577579
R= 9.Ø161877E-14
       CURRENT VALUES
X 1            4.82Ø35Ø73E-Ø7
X 2            1.41421214
X 3            1.41421557
ITERATION 48 VALUE-4.58577888
FINAL SOLUTION
X 1 = 1.67787996E-Ø7
X 2 = 1.41421214
X 3 = 1.41421555
F(X)=-4.58578261
```

7.3 References

The remarks made in the corresponding section of Chapter 4 are also appropriate here. A great amount of research work has been carried out in this area over the last three decades and much of it is still ongoing. In the last two chapters we have considered in some detail two very important constrained optimisation methods. They are of course two among many. It is hoped that the reader will be stimulated to investigate the references given, and the current literature, for much remains to be done in the search for theoretically sound and computationally practical methods for the constrained optimisation problem.

1 M. J. Box, 'A comparison of several current optimisation methods and the use of transformations in constrained problems', *Comp. Journal*, **9**, 67–77, 1966.

2 C. W. Carroll, 'The created response surface technique for optimising nonlinear restrained systems'. *Operations Research*, **9**, 169–184, 1961.

3 A. R. Colville, 'A comparative study on nonlinear programming codes', *IBM Report* No. 320–2949, 1968.

4 A. V. Fiacco and G. P. McCormick, 'The Sequential Unconstrained Minimisation Technique for nonlinear programming, a primal–dual method', *Man. Sc.*, **10**, 360–366, 1964.

5 A. V. Fiacco and G. P. McCormick, 'Computational algorithm for the Sequential Unconstrained Minimisation Technique for nonlinear programming', *Man. Sc.*, **10**, 601–617, 1964.

6 A. V. Fiacco and G. P. McCormick, 'Extensions of SUMT for nonlinear programming: equality constraints and extrapolation', *Man. Sc.*, **12**, 816–828, 1966.

7 D. Goldfarb, 'Extensions of Davidon's variable metric method to maximisation under linear inequality and equality constraints', *SIAM J. Appl. Math.*, **17**, 739–764, 1969.

Exercises 7

1 Use SUMT to minimise $f(x_1, x_2) = 3x_1^2 + 4x_1 x_2 + 5x_2^2$ where $x_1, x_2 \geqslant 0$, $x_1 + x_2 \geqslant 4$.

2 Minimise $-x_1^2 - x_2^2$ if $x_1, x_2 \geqslant 0$ and $x_1 + 2x_2 \leqslant 3$.

3 Use SUMT to solve the Post Office Parcel Problem; minimise $V = -x_1 x_2 x_3$ where $0 \leqslant x_i \leqslant 42$, $i = 1, 2, 3$ and

$$x_1 + 2x_2 + 2x_3 \leqslant 72.$$

4 Minimise, using the SUMT method, the function

$$f(x_1, x_2) = \frac{4}{x_1} + \frac{9}{x_2} + (x_1 + x_2)$$

where $x_1, x_2 \geqslant 0$, $x_1 + x_2 \leqslant S$ if (a) $S = 6$, (b) $S = 4$.

5 Minimise $f = x_1^2 + x_2^2 + x_3^2$ if $x_1 + x_2 + x_3 \geqslant 3$, $x_1 x_2 x_3 \geqslant 3$

$$x_1, x_2, x_3 \geqslant 0.$$

6 Experiment with the SUMT program by modification of (a) the initial choice of r (line 36Ø), (b) the determination of λ (line 7ØØ), (c) the reduction in r (line 161Ø).

7 Experiment with the SUMT program by modification of the convergence criteria (a) line 157Ø, (b) line 16ØØ. Try the condition IF R < IE – 12 in the latter case.

8 Show that equation 7.18 is true, viz. $f(\mathbf{x}^*_{k+1}) < f(\mathbf{x}^*_k)$.

9 Minimise $(x_1 - 1)^4 + (x_2 - 3)^2$ if $x_1, x_2 \geqslant 0$ and $3x_1^2 + 2x_2^2 \leqslant 21$, $4x_1 + 5x_2 \leqslant 20$.

10 Minimise $f(x_1, x_2) = x_1^2 + x_2^2$ subject to $x_1 \geqslant 2$, $x_1^2 - x_2^2 \leqslant 1$.

Suggestions for Further Reading

Research on optimisation is still progressing at a rapid pace. We hope that readers will have had their appetites whetted and now be ready to move on to some more recent theoretical and computational advances in the area. The list given is a small selection from many possible books and journal papers.

P. R. Adby and M. A. H. Dempster, *Introduction to Optimisation Methods*, Chapman and Hall, 1974.

D. P. Bertsekas, 'Combined primal–dual and penalty function methods,' *SIAM Journal on Control*, **13**, 521–545, 1975.

D. P. Bertsekas, *Constrained Optimisation and Lagrange Multiplier Methods*, Academic Press, 1982.

B. D. Craven, *Mathematical Programming and Control Theory*, Chapman and Hall, 1978.

J. E. Dennis and J. J. Moré, 'Quasi-Newton methods, motivation and theory', *SIAM Review*, **19**, 46–89, 1977.

R. Fletcher, 'An ideal penalty function for constrained optimisation', *J. Inst. Maths. App.*, **15**, 319–342, 1975.

P. E. Gill, W. Murray and M. H. Wainwright, *Practical Optimization*, Academic Press, 1982.

S-P. Han, 'A globally convergent method for nonlinear programming', *J. Opt. Theory App.*, **22**, 297–309, 1977.

M. R. Hestenes, *Conjugate Direction Methods in Optimization*, Springer–Verlag, 1980.

D. Q. Mayne and N. Maratos, 'A first order exact penalty function algorithm for equality constrained optimisation problems', *Math. Prog.*, **16**, 303–324, 1979.

M. J. D. Powell, 'Some convergence properties of the conjugate gradient method', *Math. Prog.*, **11**, 42–49, 1976.

M. J. D. Powell, 'Algorithms for nonlinear constraints that use Lagrangian functions', *Math. Prog.*, **14**, 224–248, 1978.

M. J. D. Powell, 'A fast algorithm for nonlinearly constrained optimisation calculations', (in *Numerical Analysis*, Edited by G. A. Watson), 144–157, Springer–Verlag, 1978.

M. J. D. Powell (Editor), *Nonlinear Optimization*, Academic Press, 1982.

D. Shanno, 'Conjugate gradient methods with inexact searches', *Maths. of Op. Res.*, **3**, 244–256, 1978.

Solutions to Exercises

Exercises 1

1 Local max. of $\frac{4}{27}$ when $x = \frac{1}{3}$; local min. of 0 when $x = 1$.

2 Max. of $\frac{1}{2}$ when $x = 1$; min. of $-\frac{1}{2}$ when $x = -1$.

3 Note $a \cos \theta + b \sin \theta \equiv \sqrt{(a^2 + b^2)} \cos (\theta - \alpha)$ where $\tan \alpha = b/a$.

4 $A = r^2 \sin 2\theta(1 + \cos 2\theta)$.

5 $f'(x)$ changes sign from −ve to +ve but $f'(0)$ is not defined.

6 0 when $x = 0$. $f'(x)$ changes sign from −ve to +ve but $f'(0)$ is not defined.

7 $-1/(3\sqrt{3})$.

9 Global min. of $-24{\cdot}3696$ at $0{\cdot}7808$, local max. of $40{\cdot}7245$ at $3{\cdot}7619$, local min. of $11{\cdot}9576$ at $5{\cdot}9572$.

10 Min. 0 at (0, 0).

11 Max. 0 at (0, 0, 0).

15 $$-2b_1 p_1 + (a_1 + a_2) p_2 + c_1 b_1 - c_2 a_2 = 0$$
$$(a_1 + a_2) p_1 - 2b_2 p_2 + c_2 b_2 - c_1 a_1 = 0.$$

16 $-0{\cdot}2766$ when $x = 0{\cdot}5885$.

Exercises 2

4 198.

5 $x = 0{\cdot}47$.

6 5·96; 12.

7 $x = 0{\cdot}47$; $f(x) = 2{\cdot}32$; 11.

9 $x = 1{\cdot}763$, $f(x) = -0{\cdot}973$.

10 Min. of 0·0465 at (0·2558, −0·1163).

15 0·5885.

Exercises 3

2 (i) 0 at (1, 2, 3) (ii) 0 at (1, 1).

6 (i) 0 at (1, 1) (ii) 0 at (0, 0, 0) (iii) 0 at (1, 10).

10 0 at (1, 0).

11 0 at (3, 2).

12 (3, 2), (3·5844, −1·8481), (−3·7793, −3·2832), (−2·8011, 3·1313).

13 $x = 1, y = 2, z = 3$ or any permutation.

14 $a = 31{\cdot}87, b = 1{\cdot}79$.

15 (i) $\ln(a) = 3{\cdot}0296$; $(a = 20{\cdot}68)$; $n = 2{\cdot}48$. (ii) $a = 22{\cdot}3, n = 2{\cdot}45$.

Exercises 4

6 Min. 0 at (4, −3, −0·5).

7 Min. 0 at (0·25, 0·75).

8 Min. 0 at (1, 0).

9 Min. 0 at (3, 2). See also Exercises 3, question 12.

10 Min. −1 at (1, 1).

Exercises 5

3 $x = \dfrac{kbc}{A}, y = \dfrac{kac}{A}, z = \dfrac{kab}{A}$ where $A = ab + bc + ca$.

5 Max. of 108 at (1, 2, 3).

7 Min. of 12·5 when $x = y = 2{\cdot}5$.

8 $x = \frac{9}{14}, y = \frac{2}{14}$, Min. $f = -\frac{371}{196}$.

13 Max. 70; min. 20.

14 If $\sqrt{\alpha} + \sqrt{\beta} \leqslant S\sqrt{\gamma}$, $x_1 = \sqrt{\dfrac{\alpha}{\gamma}}, x_2 = \sqrt{\dfrac{\beta}{\gamma}}$.

Otherwise $x_1 = \dfrac{S\sqrt{\alpha}}{\sqrt{\alpha} + \sqrt{\beta}}, x_2 = \dfrac{S\sqrt{\beta}}{\sqrt{\alpha} + \sqrt{\beta}}$.

15 $x_1 = 20, x_2 = 11, x_3 = 15$; Vol. = 3300.

16 $x_1 = 24, x_2 = 12, x_3 = 12$; Vol. = 3456.

Exercises 6

1 Min. 12·5 when $x = y = 2{\cdot}5$.

2 Min. $-\frac{371}{196}$ when $x = \frac{9}{14}, y = \frac{2}{14}$.

3 Min. 44 when $x_1 = 3, x_2 = 1$.

5 (a) $x_1 = 2, x_2 = 3$; (b) $x_1 = \frac{8}{5}, x_2 = \frac{12}{5}$.

6 Min. 1 when $x_1 = 3, x_2 = \sqrt{3}$.

7 30·24; $x_1 = 1{\cdot}7818, x_2 = 4{\cdot}4898$.

8 6·2403; $x_1 = x_2 = x_3 = 1{\cdot}4422$.

9 0; $x_1 = 3, x_2 = 4$.

10 −28·6153; $x_1 = 2{\cdot}9155, x_2 = 4{\cdot}1231, x_3 = 2{\cdot}3805$.

Exercises 7

1 44 when $x_1 = 3, x_2 = 1$.

2 −9 when $x_1 = 3, x_2 = 0$.

3 −3456 when $x_1 = 24, x_2 = 12, x_3 = 12$.

4 (a) $x_1 = 2, x_2 = 3; f = 10$ (b) $x_1 = \frac{8}{5}, x_2 = \frac{12}{5}, f = \frac{41}{4}$.

5 $f = 6{\cdot}2403; x_1 = x_2 = x_3 = 1{\cdot}4422$.

9 0 when $x_1 = 1, x_2 = 3$.

10 7 when $x_1 = 2.\ x_2 = \sqrt{3}$.

Index